NATURAL RESOURCES

Their use and abuse

David Elcome

First published in 1998 by:
Stanley Thornes (Publishers) Ltd
Ellenborough House
Wellington Street
CHELTENHAM GL50 1YW
England

98 99 00 01 02 / 10 9 8 7 6 5 4 3 2 1

A catalogue record for this book is available from the British Library.

ISBN 0-7487-3187-3

Printed and bound in Great Britain by Martins The Printers Ltd., Berwick upon Tweed

Designed by Giles Davies

Page layout and illustration by Hardlines, Charlbury, Oxfordshire

Picture research by Penni Bickle

Cover design by Sterling Associates

Acknowledgements

With thanks to the following for permission to reproduce copyright material:

Joint Nature Conservation Committee: Fig. 3.3, from Campbell, L.H., & Cooke, A.S., eds. *The indirect effects of pesticides on birds*, Peterborough, 1997; The Royal Society for the Protection of Birds: Fig. 3.4, from *Conservation Review*, Volume 2, 1988. Fig 3.5, from *Wet Grasslands – What Future?*, 1995. Fig. 3.6, from 'Agriculture in Scotland – Farming for a living', *Countryside*; Times Newspapers Limited: Fig. 4.5, *The Times*, 29 September 1997; West Sussex County Council: Fig. 2.4, from *Vision for the Wildlife of Sussex*, p.56, 1996.

David Elcombe, Figs. 7.5, 8.4 (both); Impact Photos: John Ferro Simms, Fig. 1.4; Anne-Marie Purkis, Fig. 2.5; Steve Benbow, Fig. 3.1; Skyscan, Fig. 3.2; Still Pictures, Figs. 1.5, 2.3, 3.7, 3.8 (both), 3.9, 4.7, 4.8, 5.5, 5.7, 5.9, 7.8, 9.1; Topham Picturepoint, Figs. 2.6, 6.12; Trip Photography, Figs. 1.1, 7.2, 8.6.

Every effort has been made to contact copyright holders. The publishers apologise to anyone whose rights have been inadvertently overlooked, and will be happy to rectify any errors or omissions.

Contents

Introduction

SECTION A

What are natural resources?

Natural resources are all the natural commodities and features of the Earth's physical environment that are exploited by the human population. They are used to provide our **needs** – the food, water and other materials that are essential to keep us alive. They also satisfy our **wants** – those things that, although not absolutely necessary for our survival, are the 'extras' that support particular life-styles or standards of living.

Figure 1.1 Planet Earth from outer space

For something to become a **resource** it must be a material or characteristic that people find useful or desirable. Just how useful something is will depend upon its location and on human know-how. Where does it occur and how easy is it to exploit? What is it needed for? Do people have the knowledge, technology and economic resources needed to exploit it? It is questions such as these that are involved in resource use. But the perception and evaluation of resources change over time. For example, to Neolithic people flint was a fundamental and highly valued natural resource used to make axes and other basic tools. The level of technology at that time was primitive. People had no knowledge of, or use for, most of the resources that we now consider essential (uranium or crude oil, for example). However, in today's technologically advanced society flint has little value. We only use it for hard-core in road making or as a decorative building stone.

It is the physical environment that provides us with our life support system and all the resources we use **(1.1)**. This environment has evolved over millions of years, but it is finely balanced and easily disrupted by human activity.

The Earth's physical environment is made up of four major sections or spheres **(1.2)**:

- the **atmosphere** – the 100km thick layer of gases that surrounds the Earth
- the **hydrosphere** – the Earth's various water bodies, namely the seas and oceans, lakes, rivers, ice sheets, glaciers, lying snow, water stored in the rocks and soil, as well as water vapour in the atmosphere and suspended as droplets in clouds and fog banks
- the **lithosphere** – the rocks and soils that make up the Earth's crust
- the **biosphere** – those parts of the other three spheres in which all living things exist and interact.

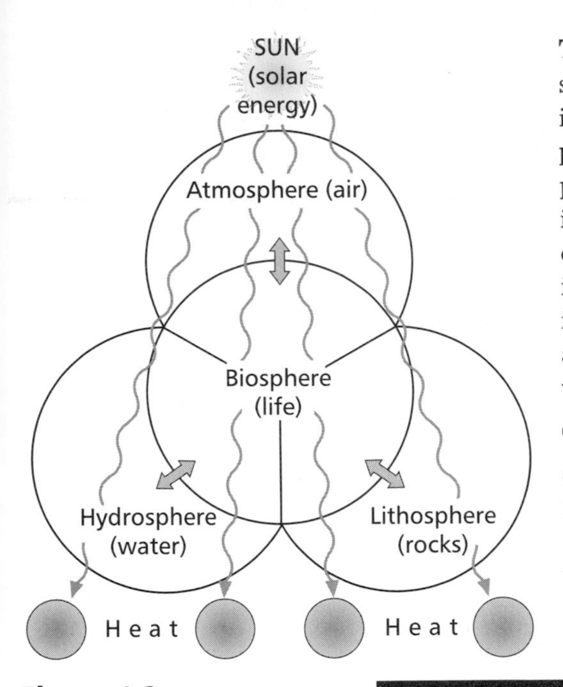

Figure 1.2
The four spheres

The biosphere acts as a bridge between the other three spheres and is dependent upon them through a range of interactions, the most important of which is the process of **photosynthesis**. Life on Earth only exists because of this process and all living things are dependent directly or indirectly upon it for their existence. The process uses carbon dioxide from the atmosphere, and releases oxygen in exchange, thus helping to maintain the balance of gases in the atmosphere. It takes water from the hydrosphere and nutrients and minerals from the lithosphere, all of which are recycled by the processes of decay.

Together these four spheres make up the Earth's life support system. They provide us with all our natural resources, with air and water, climate and soil, fossil fuels and other forms of energy, minerals, **biodiversity** (the variety of species and the genetic diversity of plants and animals) and landscape. These are the things on which human survival and development depend.

Review

1 Illustrate your understanding of the differences between a **need** and a **want** by providing three examples of each.

2 Identify three natural resources obtained from the biosphere.

3 Explain why the process of photosynthesis, which takes place in the cells of green plants, is fundamental to resources obtained from the biosphere.

SECTION B

Renewable and non-renewable resources

An important distinction is made between those natural resources that are **renewable** and those that are **non-renewable** or finite **(1.3)**. Renewable resources are of two kinds:

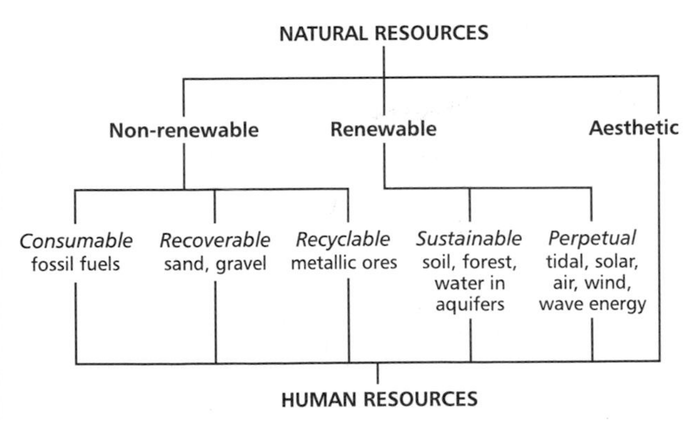

Figure 1.3 A classification of natural resources

1 Those that are largely unaffected by human activities and are perpetual or continuous; resources such as solar and tidal energy, waves and flowing water.
2 Those that have the potential to be abused by people, including climate, air, water, soil and landscape. Although their distribution across the planet may be very uneven, they appear to be everlasting and constantly recur over time. However, their quality may be easily damaged, for example through pollution, erosion or other abuse.

Renewable resources include those whose use is **sustainable**. This means they are assets that can be constantly and successfully recovered, re-used or recycled, or which by careful management, including replanting, replenishment or good husbandry, can be maintained indefinitely for future use. If a resource is to be sustainable, the rate of its exploitation must not exceed that for its renewal.

In contrast, resources such as the fossil fuels (coal, oil and natural gas) and those minerals that cannot be recycled, are classed as **non-renewable, finite** or **stock resources**. Due to the ever-increasing demands of people, the reserves or stocks of these resources are being depleted and will eventually run out. Once consumed they are gone for ever.

The **reserves** of a resource are the proportion of the known stock that has the potential to be exploited by people at current levels of scientific understanding and technology. The rates of use are strongly influenced by the quality of human and economic resources available. For example, large deposits of coal are known to occur in the rocks of Antarctica but at the present time, and indeed for the foreseeable future, they are not a potentially exploitable reserve owing to:

- the difficulties of operating in such a harsh climate
- extreme damage to the environment if the deposits were to be exploited
- the very high costs of transport from such a remote place to major centres of population and industry
- lack of an available workforce
- the international agreement to leave Antartica's minerals untouched.

Case study: Oil and natural gas

Figure 1.4
A North Sea oil rig

North Sea oil and natural gas

The reserves of oil and natural gas that lie beneath the bed of the North Sea were once thought to be too difficult and too expensive to be worth exploiting. However, since the late 1970s there have been major advances in offshore drilling techniques, combined with worldwide shortages, politically motivated price increases for oil and natural gas, and rising demand. These factors have made the extraction of oil and natural gas from beneath the stormy waters of the North Sea both possible and economically feasible **(1.4)**. Thus they have acquired **reserve** status.

At current rates of extraction, the known reserves of oil and natural gas beneath the North Sea will be largely exhausted by the year 2010. This has forced oil companies such as BP to re-appraise the potential of **stocks** that have been discovered in even more difficult locations. These include those located below the deep and stormy waters of the North Atlantic. The technological lessons learned from the extraction of North

Sea oil and gas are now being applied to the seabed in waters more than 500 metres deep, as for example in BP's Foinavon Field 160km to the west of Shetland. These stocks would not have been workable a few years ago. Now though a new technology has been developed whereby drilling and extraction can be carried out from vessels rather than rigs using flexible bits and pipes. The crucial technique here is the ability to keep such a vessel anchored accurately and securely over the wellhead.

Oil-sand deposits in Alberta

These deposits have been known for many years, but the cost of extracting oil from them has been considered far too great until now. With the depletion of Canada's conventional crude oil reserves and the development of modern technology, the extraction of oil from these bitumen-rich sands has now become economically viable. Both Mobil Oil Canada and Shell Canada are building plants in Alberta's Athabasca region to extract oil from the deposits. Production is expected to begin in 2002 and within a few years the region could be supplying over 50 per cent of Canada's oil output. It could also supply markets in the USA.

When defining natural resources, it is possible to distinguish a further subgroup described as **aesthetic resources (1.3)**. These include physical qualities of the environment such as a stunning landscape or the beauty of nature **(1.5)**. Also in this category are attributes of a human origin like our cultural and historical heritage. While aesthetic resources may not be essential to keeping us alive, they do exert a substantial influence on our quality of life.

Figure 1.5
An aesthetic resource: mountain and lake scenery in Canada

Economic and human resources differ from natural resources, including aesthetic resources. They must be available if a natural resource is to be developed or exploited. **Economic resources** are largely to do with finance and capital. **Human resources** include such aspects as:

- the size of the population
- the level of technological development
- the availability of labour
- managerial and technical skills
- the ability of individuals to organise, innovate and communicate
- the degree of accessibility provided by transport facilities.

Review

4 Make a list of ten natural resources.
  a Consider each of these and decide whether it is a renewable or a non-renewable resource.
  b For each resource, state whether its origin is in the lithosphere, the atmosphere, the hydrosphere or the biosphere.
  c Decide whether each of the resources you have listed is a need or a want.

5 With reference to natural resources, explain the differences between a **reserve** and a **stock**.

6 With reference to the two case studies above, what are the factors that have encouraged people to look for new reserves of oil and natural gas?

7 Identify at least five aspects of our historical and cultural heritage that qualifies them for the description 'aesthetic resources'. Give some examples.

8 Explain what is meant by 'sustainable use of natural resources'. Illustrate your answer with reference to three named resources.

SECTION C

The human ecological footprint

Unfortunately, the exploitation of natural resources threatens, and often actually causes serious damage to one or more of the spheres that make up the natural environment. One major cause of the accelerating degradation of the environment is the rapid growth of the human population. Another is human greed and the desire for short-term economic gain that, too often, takes precedence over other, long-term considerations.

It is also the case that the impact made by people on the global environment as they consume natural resources is far greater for those living in the rich industrial nations than for those living in lower-income countries. This impact on the environment has been called the **ecological footprint**. It is a reflection of the developed world's high standard of living and high levels of consumption. The basic needs for human survival are taken for granted, but in the developed world a great emphasis is put on satisfying **wants**. The possession of certain material goods and the enjoyment of particular services are regarded as being highly desirable, but are not essential for keeping us alive. The demand for these commodities and comforts is artificially stimulated by marketing through the mass media, advertising and fashion.

The Netherlands provides a striking example of the size of the ecological footprint of a developed society. By importing produce from lower-income, less developed countries, its population consumes an output equivalent to 14 times as much productive land as is contained within its own frontiers. Similar statistics could be quoted for most other developed countries.

Case study: The Dutch global ecological footprint

The Netherlands is located on the North Sea coast and on the delta of the Rhine. It is therefore in an ideal position for trade. Consequently, the Dutch economy is largely directed towards foreign trade and industry. Although the area of the country is small, the population is over 15 million. The Netherlands can therefore only maintain its high standard of living through overseas trade. However, its dependence on overseas goods has an impact on the environment in those countries with which it trades, and many of the resulting developments are not sustainable in the long term.

Timber and the Netherlands

Timber provides an excellent example of the Dutch ecological footprint. The Netherlands has little in the way of forest resources and therefore it depends on importing the timber it needs. Each year Finland fells 40.3 million m^3 of timber, 1.0 million m^3 of which goes to the Netherlands. An area of 13 800ha needs to be logged each year just to meet the Dutch demand. This in turn means that 400 000ha of forest have be maintained in Finland for the Netherlands alone if its annual demand is to be supported on a sustainable basis.

However, the Netherlands also has a major demand for tropical hardwoods. The total Dutch import amounts to 3.5 million m^3 per year, much of which is supplied by Malaysia. Meeting the Dutch demand requires 25 000ha of tropical rainforest to be logged annually in Malaysia, and 800 000ha of forest is required to meet this demand year on year. Malaysia's current timber production policies do not allow biodiversity to be maintained; it is producing timber at five times the rate that is sustainable.

The Dutch demand for tapioca

Although it is densely populated, 60 per cent of the area of the Netherlands is farmland, and the country is the world's fourth largest exporter of agricultural products. However, Dutch farming cannot survive without imported agricultural inputs. Every hectare of Dutch farmland is dependent upon the agricultural outputs of 7ha of cultivated land in other countries. For example, 2.5 million tonnes of tapioca are imported annually into the Netherlands just to feed cattle. Tapioca is made from cassava and most of the Dutch imports come from Thailand. This requires an area of 450 000ha to be cultivated in Thailand to supply the requirements of domestic cattle farming in the Netherlands. The total area of cassava production in Thailand has increased from 100 000ha in 1965 to 1.5 million ha in 1994.

This has an impact on biodiversity in Thailand. As cassava fetches a high price, many Thai farmers have switched to a cassava monoculture in order to reap the financial rewards. Monoculture degrades the soil and so the pressure to bring new land into cultivation increases. This means bringing virgin land – often rainforest – into cultivation, thus reducing the area of this globally important habitat and its biodiversity.

Indicator	Units	1950	1991	% change
Grain production	m tonnes	631	1696	270
Soya production	m tonnes	18	106	590
Meat production	m tonnes	46	173	380
Fish catches	m tonnes	22	97	440
Irrigated area	m hectares	95	235	250
Fertiliser use	m tonnes	14	136	970
Oil production	m barrels/day	10	59	590
Natural gas production	trillion cu. ft	7	77	1100
Motor car production	millions	8	35	440

Figure 1.6 Some indicators of growth in the global consumption of resources, 1950–91

The statistics in **1.6** indicate the rapid increase in global resource consumption. They imply ever-increasing demands on the Earth's physical environment and natural resources. The size of the human ecological footprint is becoming bigger by the day. The pressures go hand in hand with the diverse demands of settlement and urbanisation, from supplies of water and building materials to land for recreation and farming. The ability of the global environment to meet these demands – the Earth's **carrying capacity** – may already have been exceeded. Currently under increasing threat are:

- many aspects of the Earth's climatic system, through the greenhouse effect, acid rain and destruction of the ozone layer
- the hydrological cycle damaged by pollution, over-abstraction from aquifers and surface stores, construction of major reservoirs and by climatic change
- biodiversity reduced by pollution, destruction of natural habitats and ecosystems, monoculture in agriculture and timber production
- nutrient cycles damaged by habitat loss, soil erosion and salinisation
- landscape quality lost by intensive cultivation, mineral extraction, excessive tourist pressure, urban and industrial development
- reserves of fossil fuels and other minerals through exhaustion of known or most easily accessible deposits.

If people are to live in a sustainable relationship with the natural environment and its resources, they must moderate the inevitable pressures placed on the four spheres as their numbers continue to grow. They must also change their practices. Exploitation needs to be steered more towards renewable resources.

While human exploitation of the Earth's natural resources is a major cause of change in the atmosphere, hydrosphere and biosphere, it must be remembered that natural processes also create environmental change. In some cases, people are merely exacerbating the effects of these natural changes. For example, during the last 100 years there has been a build-up of artificial chemicals in the atmosphere, such as the CFCs (chlorofluorocarbons) that have been partly responsible for thinning the ozone layer. Equally, volcanoes have emitted vast quantities of ozone-destroying gases and others chemicals and these have also contributed to the greenhouse effect and global warming.

Enquiry

1 a Explain what is meant by the **human ecological footprint**.
  b Why is the ecological footprint of a person living in a more developed country likely to be larger than that of someone living in a less developed country?

2 With reference to the case study of the Dutch global ecological footprint, suggest three ways in which the environmental impact of their consumption of **a)** timber and **b)** tapioca might be reduced.

3 In small groups within your class, discuss the proposition: 'Whether or not something is considered to be a resource depends upon the technology and economic resources available to a community.'
Each group should list the key points agreed in their discussion, perhaps on a flip chart, and refer to specific examples. Report back on the group's conclusions to the whole class.

CHAPTER 2

Biodiversity as a natural resource

SECTION A

What is biodiversity?

Biodiversity, or strictly speaking **biological diversity**, refers to the variety of life. It includes all living things: fungi, plants, reptiles, mammals, birds, fish, insects and many other invertebrates and micro-organisms. Biodiversity is created by the immense number of living species and by genetic variation within individual species. Also contributing are the many different ecosystems and habitats that make up the Earth's biosphere. Each of these has its own associated community of plants and animals.

Life on Earth has been evolving for more than 3000 million years. It continues to do so. No one knows exactly how many species there are at present. So far 1.8 million have been described and named by science, but one estimate suggests there could be as many as 30 million. This huge variety of living things reflects the geological, climatic and other environmental differences that occur on this planet. Every habitat contains an array of plant and animal species adapted to the physical conditions found within it. These species live together as ecological communities – some are **producers** (i.e. they manufacture food by the process of photosynthesis), others are **consumers**. Some of these consumers are predators, others are prey. Each is dependent on the presence of many other species. This interdependence of species underpins the complex diversity of life that exists across the planet as a whole; people are just one part of the system.

Review

1 With reference to one specific ecosystem, produce a labelled diagram on which the main producers and consumers are identified.

SECTION B

The importance of biodiversity as a natural resource

Our planet's goods and services depend on the variety and variability of genes, species, populations and ecosystems. Biological resources feed and clothe us and provide housing, medicines and spiritual nourishment. The natural ecosystems of forest, savannah, pasture and rangeland, desert, tundra, river, lake and sea contain most of the Earth's biodiversity. . . The current decline in biodiversity is largely the result of human activity and represents a serious threat to human development. The available evidence indicates that human activities are eroding biological resources and greatly reducing the planet's biological diversity.

From Chapter 15, *Agenda 21* of the Earth Summit in Rio de Janeiro, 1992

Figure 2.1 The importance of biodiversity . . .

The Earth's genes, species and ecosystems are the products of over 3 billion years of evolution, and are the basis of the survival of our own species. Biological diversity is valuable because future practical uses and values are unpredictable, because variety is inherently interesting and more attractive and because our understanding of ecosystems is insufficient to be certain of the impact of removing any component.

The loss of biodiversity is due above all to economic factors, especially the low values given to biodiversity and ecological functions such as watershed protection, nutrient cycling, pollution control, soil formation, photosynthesis and evolution. Biodiversity is very much a cross-sectoral issue, and virtually all sectors have an interest in its conservation and the sustainable use of its components. Biological resources are renewable and with proper management can support human needs indefinitely. These resources and the diversity of the systems which support them, are therefore the essential foundation of sustainable development.

From *A Guide to the Convention on Biological Diversity, Environmental Policy and Law,* IUCN,1994

Figure 2.2
. . . as a natural resource

The quotations in **2.1** and **2.2** are taken from documents agreed by the leaders of most nations. They indicate that biodiversity is itself a natural resource. It is a vital part of the Earth's life-support system. People are dependent on biodiversity for so many things that are part of everyday life. Without it we would soon perish. The biosphere and its biodiversity provides us with:

- the food we eat, both animal and vegetable
- timber for building, furniture, fencing, tools and paper
- fibres for clothing, string and rope
- drugs and medicines
- resins for glues and other uses
- aesthetic and spiritual satisfaction and enjoyment.

By maintaining a rich biodiversity we safeguard these resources for the future. At the same time, we insure ourselves against potential agricultural disaster and disease. Biodiversity provides the genetic bank on which we may need to draw in the future. We may require different genetic material for use in plant- and animal-breeding programmes to:

- increase food production
- protect crops and livestock from pests
- improve climatic tolerance such as drought- or frost-resistance
- produce natural cures for many human ailments and diseases.

We can never be certain what might be of practical value in the future, so any loss of biodiversity now will restrict future choices. Biodiversity is also an important aesthetic resource. It provides opportunities for academic research and enquiry, spiritual satisfaction and recreational pleasure. Thus it is a resource of immense ethical value, but one that is hard to measure in terms of economic value other than as a major factor in promoting 'green' tourism.

Review

2 Write a short account explaining why the conservation of biodiversity is crucial to human survival.

3 'Biodiversity provides the genetic bank on which we may need to draw in the future.' Using at least three examples, explain what this means.

4 Why is it that ecological succession often leads to a natural reduction in biodiversity?

SECTION C

The impact of human activities on biodiversity

As well as being a vital natural resource, biodiversity is valuable as an indicator of the health of an environment. If the rate of change in biodiversity is greater than might be expected from normal evolutionary causes – that is, from ecological succession – then it is likely that the ecosystem is ailing. It will have been thrown out of balance. For example, some species may become pests. In most cases, this damage is caused by human activities.

Changes to biodiversity are usually incidental or unintended side-effects of human activities. We would prefer it if they did not happen but in all probability no thought was given to the impact of those activities on biodiversity in the first place. Agriculture, forestry and fishing directly exploit the biosphere and its diversity and can easily have an adverse effect. So too do mining and quarrying, as they exploit and spoil the lithosphere. Similar degradation occurs in the hydrosphere as wetlands are drained, water tables lowered and irrigation schemes implemented. Many of these same activities have an impact on the atmosphere. In its turn, air pollution can add to acid rain and climatic change.

Natural ecosystems are shrinking as a result of human activities. As a consequence, pressure on the remaining natural habitats continues to increase; the number of species they contain continues to go down. Habitat destruction is driving species to extinction. Among the planet's birds and mammals – probably the best known biological groups – current rates of extinction are estimated to be 100 to 1000 times greater than they would be under natural conditions. We are tampering with the ecology of our planet – our life support system – and drastically altering a system that is still not fully understood. As many conservation organisations claim, we may be taking a big risk with our future.

Case study: The biodiversity of Madagascar

The island of Madagascar, located in the Indian Ocean to the east of southern Africa, has a huge diversity of natural species. It is estimated that before human habitation of the island more than 300 000 species existed here. There were several reasons for this immense biodiversity:

- Madagascar became geographically split off from the rest of Africa about 180 million years ago with the break-up of Gondwanaland. This permitted evolution to continue in isolation from the rest of the planet so that **endemic species** (i.e. unique to Madagascar) evolved.
- There was a wide variety of habitats created by the central mountain range, and its influence on the island's microclimates. These range from semi-desert to tropical rainforest.
- People arrived here relatively late, about 2000 years ago.

Figure 2.3 Forest destruction in Madagascar

Since the arrival of people, there has been a major disruption of the natural ecosystems, with the loss of as many as 100 000 species. Forests in particular have been lost due to fire, clearance for agriculture, logging and the collection of fuelwood. Losses continue as trees are felled illegally, and rare plant and animal species of plant and animal are smuggled out.

Today, yet another threat faces Madagascar's biodiversity. A mineral sand known as ilmenite occurs beneath sand dunes in the south-east of the island. This is a natural resource from which titanium dioxide is extracted, a brilliant white pigment used in the manufacture of such everyday products as cosmetics, toothpaste and white paint. The Rio Tinto Zinc Company proposes extracting the mineral from beneath the dunes. This will destroy the remaining 4000ha of coastal forest, a unique biological community that currently covers the dunes.

'It is essential that the world realises the biological importance of the island and the plight of its people and hurries to the rescue of this extraordinary corner of the globe,' wrote Gerald Durrell in 1994. But how can this be achieved?

- Should the destruction be allowed to continue?
- Does the answer lie in increased tourism and turning Madagascar into a sort of natural botanic and zoological garden – a living museum?
- Should there be a huge programme to promote environmental education and sustainable practices?
- Or is a mixture of these required so that Madagascar's unique wildlife has a value to the local people and they are empowered to develop their own solutions to the problem?

SECTION D

Treating the causes of biodiversity decline

Declining biodiversity is a symptom of sickness in the Earth's ecosystems. Like any doctor treating a sick patient, it is not just a matter of relieving unpleasant symptoms. The root causes of the disease need to be attacked. Some of the remedial treatments that are necessary will affect our daily lives and life-styles. To reduce atmospheric pollution, for example, we will need to reduce drastically our dependence on the motor car, and make much more efficient use of public transport.

The many benefits that biodiversity can bring to people cannot be sustained unless the biological resource is itself maintained. Slowing the loss of biodiversity requires greater understanding of its role in ecosystems and its importance for human life. Conversely, increased understanding of biodiversity calls for the study of representative and viable samples of ecosystems, species and populations. This is best done through a worldwide network of reserves, gene banks, botanical and zoological gardens. Developing a sustainable use of biodiversity requires a detailed knowledge and understanding of biological resources. That knowledge and understanding is to be found in both modern research and traditional practices.

Case study: Conserving biodiversity on heathlands in Sussex

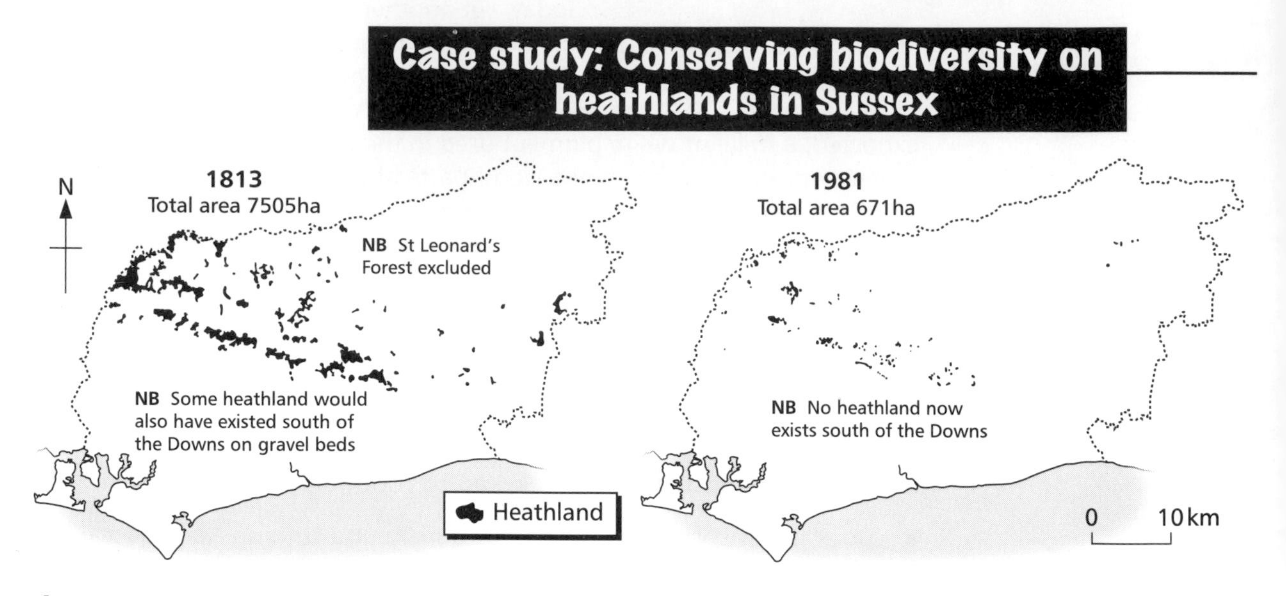

Figure 2.4
Heathland decline in West Sussex, 1813–1981

The heathlands of southern England are a habitat created by human activity. Although these areas were originally invaded by woodland following the amelioration of climate at the end of the Pleistocene Ice Age, the arrival of people herding browsing animals and practising cultivation on the light sandy soils of the Lower Greensand and the Ashdown Forest Ridge soon reduced the forest cover. This resulted in the leaching of nutrients from the soil to give acidic podsols either dominated by heather and gorse where grazing predominated, or invaded by bracken, birch and Scots pine elsewhere. The vegetation is prone to fire in drought years, however, and this can be an important factor in maintaining open heath. In the valleys, there are bog communities.

They have come to support a unique assemblage of animal species, many of which are on the northernmost extent of their range in Britain. They include such birds as the Dartford warbler, stonechat, nightjar and woodlark; the very rare sand lizard and smooth snake; and insects such as the silver-studded blue butterfly and the emperor moth.

Heathlands have decreased rapidly in Sussex during the last 100 years **(2.4)**. In 1813 West Sussex alone had some 7500ha of heathland, but this had declined to just 671ha by 1981 due to agricultural

Review

5 Explain why regular burning and grazing are necessary if the biodiversity of the heathland ecosystem is to be maintained.

6 Suggest at least three other human pressures that threaten the heathlands of southern England.

improvement, afforestation and building. The greatest threat today is fragmentation of the remaining blocks. Reduced grazing by commoners' animals means less check on encroachment of the heath by birch and Scots pine. Enrichment of the nutrient-poor soils is also a problem. This comes from traffic fumes containing nitrogen oxides, from fertiliser dust particles drifting from fertilisers applied on nearby farmland, and from ammonia created by livestock farms. These cause conversion of heather-rich communities to grass-dominated heaths.

The Sussex Wildlife Trust aims to expand the area of heathland on sites where it once occurred and to encourage sympathetic management. There is also an incentive scheme for removing conifers and other trees, increasing grazing by deer, cattle and ponies and preventing further expansion of settlement onto heathland areas.

If this can be achieved, the unique biodiversity of southern heathland can be retained for future generations.

SECTION E

Forestry and its exploitation of biodiversity

Much of the Earth's biodiversity occurs in its forests and woodlands. The tropical rainforests, for example, have been evolving for over 30 million years and possibly contain as many as a half of the world's plant and animal species – a huge assemblage of interdependent organisms. Almost every nook and cranny of a tropical rainforest is occupied by something that grows.

Forests also perform many vital ecological roles such as maintaining the oxygen balance, transpiring water vapour to the atmosphere, protecting watersheds and soils from erosion, and providing habitats for much of the world's biodiversity. Wherever they occur, forests and woodlands are an important natural resource. They provide people with timber for making buildings and furniture, pulp for paper, fuelwood, raw materials for medicines, and products such as nuts, rubber and resins.

In the UK, woodlands once covered around two-thirds of the total land area. Over thousands of years, these forests have been cleared and exploited by people so that by 1900 their extent had been reduced to about 5 per cent of the original area. Today the figure is nearer 10 per cent due to new plantations. However, many of these plantations consist of alien conifer species and lack the biodiversity of the native woodland. Only 2.6 per cent is original 'ancient' woodland.

Case study: Sustainable forestry in Finland

Perhaps because two-thirds of their homeland is covered by forests, the Finnish people place a huge cultural and spiritual value on their coniferous forests. They are also a major economic resource, contributing over 8 per cent to Finland's gross national product (GNP) and accounting for more than 5 per cent of the country's earnings from exports.

Figure 2.5 A Finnish paper mill by a 'clean' lake

Sustainable management is now the key to the future of Finland's forests. Of the total area of 20 million ha, about 350 000ha is felled annually, providing 40.3 million m^3 of timber. Only small blocks are cleared at a time – usually areas smaller than 2ha and only very rarely as much as 10ha. Cutting regular shapes in the forest cover is not permitted and great care is taken to preserve biodiversity. As far as possible, marshes within the forests, areas close to streams, and rocky outcrops, are left untouched. The regeneration of cleared areas aims to encourage mixed forest, with willows and birch as well as native conifers. Little or no fertiliser is added.

However, the Finns are very conscious of the environmental impact of their forestry operations. These include not just the felling of trees but in particular the conversion of wood into pulp for paper. This process uses large quantities of water. Organic waste discharged into lakes and rivers causes **eutrophication**, whilst the emission of sulphur compounds results in atmospheric pollution.

Review

7 Find out the meaning of **eutrophication**.

8 Draw and label a diagram to show the consequences for the environment of papermaking.

Since 1980, Finland has made outstanding progress in reducing the problems:

- the amount of water used in the processing of pulp has been reduced by 75 per cent
- organic contaminants have been reduced by 15 per cent
- atmospheric sulphur emissions have been cut by nearly 80 per cent.

Nevertheless, conservationists point out that pollution levels are still too high. They also stress the fact that many ancient trees are felled annually, some being 200 to 300 years old, and Finnish companies have destroyed huge tracts of forest in Karelia, Russia.

Case study: Forests and biodiversity in India

A small number of countries, most of them in the tropics, account for a very high proportion of the world's biodiversity. India is among 12 nations that between them account for up to 70 per cent of the world total. In particular, the forests of the Western Ghats – a mountain chain that runs the length of western India from north to south – contain a large number of endemic species of plants, birds, mammals, reptiles and butterflies.

Although satellite pictures of the Indian subcontinent show that over 17 per cent of the land area is under forest, much of it monsoon deciduous forest, a closer look reveals that only 12 per cent of this is dense cover. At ground level, it can be seen that plantation monoculture of alien species, such as rubber and eucalyptus, predominates. These areas lack a rich ground cover and have a poor biodiversity.

India faces many problems of overpopulation, overgrazing, poverty and unplanned development. Demands for land, water and energy continue to grow with the rapid increase in population. This puts increasing pressure on the country's few remaining biodiversity hot-spots.

A classic example is provided by impoverished tribal areas where millions of forest dwellers are forced to cut and sell fuelwood in order to obtain enough money to prevent their families from starving **(2.6)**. Traditionally, Indian tribal people have lived in harmony with the forest, their hunting and gathering activities and their limited attempts at cultivation being sustainable. However, the forest areas have diminished with commercial logging and widespread clearance for agriculture, mining, urban development and industry. As a result, many tribal peoples have been forced to adopt new life-styles in the forest that remains, and to exploit it in various unsustainable ways.

Figure 2.6 Trees being cut for fuelwood

In the national park at Borivili, on the northern edge of Mumbai (Bombay), the tribal women get up before dawn and may walk many kilometres into the retreating forest to illegally gather their heavy headloads of fuelwood. This must then be carried a considerable distance to the settlements at the edge of the park where it is sold for a few rupees. Thus there is a strong link between the people's poverty, habitat degradation and loss of biodiversity. So what can be done to solve the problem?

One answer may be for the Forest Department to enforce the law more strictly. But the people are faced with little choice. They either exploit the remaining forest or face starvation. Resettlement could be another answer, but to where? How would people earn a living?

Perhaps one solution lies in giving the people more freedom and control over their surroundings. Replanting degraded areas with native plants is an obvious first step, along with education programmes explaining the need for sustainability. Providing outlets for sustainably harvested medicinal plants and encouraging beneficial activities such as bee-keeping for the commercial sale of wax and honey would be other vital steps.

Support is also needed for the Indian custom of 'sacred groves'. These are a traditional, if unintended, means of preserving biodiversity, and a good future source of plant genetic material. They range in area from less than a hectare to several square kilometres. They are protected by local people because they are believed to be inhabited by ancestral spirits and deities. It is taboo for such groves to be damaged, although this has often been ignored by commercial forestry interests. Where they flourish, sacred groves have become sanctuaries for wildlife, and important in water and soil retention.

Review

9 With other students, debate the statement: 'Since India's forests are a renewable resource, people should be allowed to exploit them as they have done for centuries.'

Case study: Damage to the Black Forest by acid rain

In Germany's Black Forest some 250 000 jobs are dependent on forestry activities and tourism. However, the forest is not only of major importance to the local economy, it also protects groundwater supplies, prevents soil erosion, conserves a wide range of wild plant and animal species, and influences local climatic conditions.

Now, though, the biodiversity of the forest is being damaged. Since the mid-1970s many mature silver fir and spruce trees have died or become badly diseased as a result of air pollution and acid rain (see **Chapter 6**). The main pollutants are sulphur dioxide (SO_2), nitrogen oxides (NO_x) and low-level ozone (O_3). The first two of these gases reach the ground as acid rain which then penetrates the litter of leaf-needles on the forest floor **(2.7)**. The percolating water dissolves humic acids within that litter and so becomes even more acidic. While the acidity itself may be a problem, it also releases heavy metals into the ground and these are noxious to the trees.

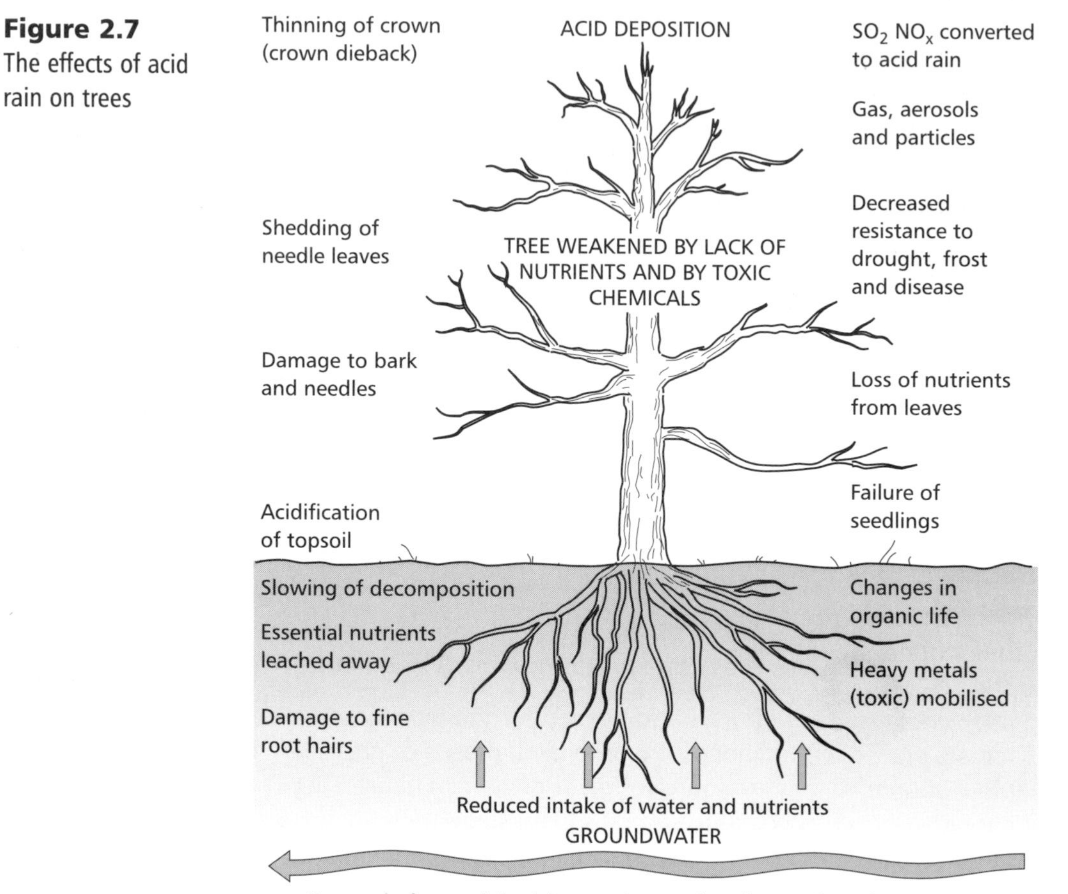

Figure 2.7
The effects of acid rain on trees

The only effective counter-measure to this destruction of the forest is a rapid and drastic reduction in the emission of air pollutants, especially sulphur dioxide. This is an international problem, since the source of many of the pollutants lies outside Germany. In this case, the full cooperation of the German, Swiss and French governments is required, as well as that of more distant states such as the Czech Republic.

Enquiry

1. **a** Find out the main sources of sulphur dioxide which is causing acid rain.
   b How feasible is it to reduce the amount that is released into the atmosphere?

2. Explain why it might be difficult to reach international agreements to reduce acid rain.

3. **a** Produce a table headed 'Causes of biodiversity loss', listing the range of causes under the subheadings 'Human causes' and 'Natural causes'. Which is the longer list?
   b Produce a list of actions that could be taken to reduce biodiversity loss. How many of these are personal actions that you could take?
   c Produce a list of the consequences to the human population if biodiversity loss is allowed to continue.

4. Consider each of the questions raised at the end of the case study on Madagascar (pages 14–15). Justify the answers you give to each of them.
   You may like to seek the views of international conservation organisations such as Greenpeace, Friends of the Earth and WWF (World Wide Fund for Nature) on these issues. (If you write to organisations of this kind be sure to include a large stamped addressed envelope for their reply and allow time for it to be delivered.)
   You may also find viewpoints expressed in such publications as *New Scientist* and *The New Internationalist*, which are available in most larger public libraries.

5. What are the pros and cons of the production and use of recycled paper as a way of reducing human demand for forest resources?
   Read background articles on this topic in such publications as *New Scientist*. Seek the views of conservation organisations and major paper producers such as Reeds and Bowaters. Does your school have an 'environmental policy'? Does it encourage the recycling of waste paper and use of recycled products?

CHAPTER 3

Natural resources and food production

SECTION A

Natural resources used to produce food

Although fish also forms a part of our diet (see **Chapter 4**), it is the world's farmers who must provide the main food requirements of the world's growing and increasingly affluent population. The nature of farm outputs in any one area is influenced by its natural resources. These include the amount of land available and its physical character, particularly the nature of its soils and climate. Agriculture also exploits the biosphere, particularly its biodiversity, and in doing so has a major impact upon it.

As well as being influenced by the natural resources of the physical environment, the actual crops grown and livestock reared by a farmer are strongly conditioned by economic and human factors, especially:

- consumer demand, which helps determine the profitability of particular crops and products
- the availability and cost of labour
- the technology available, including farm machinery, fertilisers, pesticides, types of seed and livestock
- the economic, social and agricultural policies of the government and the price mechanisms under which they operate
- the distance of the farm from the consumers of its produce, which has a direct impact on transport costs.

Figure 3.1 Food displays in a British supermarket

Societies must be able to supply sufficient food for the survival of their people, but in today's world few countries are self-sufficient. This is particularly true of developed countries. Take a look at the range of products on the shelves of any supermarket **(3.1)**. It is immediately apparent that there is a huge worldwide trade in food commodities. Relatively few of the foods eaten in the UK are produced there. Indeed, agricultural production now accounts for less than 5 per cent of the UK's gross domestic product (GDP).

The agriculture industry is creating environmental problems by using natural resources for food production in unsustainable ways. Sustainable development is about balancing the limitations of the environment against the demands of maximum production, human nutritional needs and the economic well-being of society, now and in the future. The land and soils used for agriculture are only renewable resources if the crops and livestock are harvested and managed in sustainable ways. Modern agricultural techniques harm soil quality in many ways, for example by:

- clearing vegetation and exposing soils to the ravages of wind and rain
- compaction by farm machinery
- monoculture that strips away soil nutrients with every harvest
- irrigation which causes salinisation in semi-arid areas.

In addition, a cocktail of chemicals – artificial fertilisers and pesticides – is poured onto the land to increase its productivity and to maximise profits. These abuses of soil as a natural resource are leading to lost fertility and soil erosion, to desertification in some areas and flooding in others. Water and air are polluted, while destruction of natural habitats reduces biodiversity and causes landscape degradation.

Review

1 Produce a table listing the main economic and human factors that might influence a farmer in his choice of crops and/or livestock.

SECTION B

The European Common Agricultural Policy

In the European Union (EU), the Common Agricultural Policy (CAP) encourages high inputs, intensive use of the land and monoculture (the same crop grown year after year on a large scale). It has been the cause of major and rapid changes to agricultural practices, wildlife and the landscape. In economic terms, it has also created problems of over-production and surpluses – the so-called 'wine lakes' and 'food mountains'. On the other hand, it has ensured that high-quality food supplies are available for the EU's population and that there are few shortages.

The countryside of the UK has been shaped largely by its history and its use by people over many centuries. It has always changed to meet social and economic needs. In spite of the country having a highly urbanised society, over 75 per cent of the UK's land area is used for food production.

Since the Second World War, government policies have strongly influenced the UK's agricultural industry. These have aimed to encourage farmers to modernise and produce more food. Since the UK became part of the European Economic Community (now the EU) in 1973, support for agriculture has largely come from the CAP through **intervention buying**. Under this system, the food produced is purchased at an agreed minimum price regardless of the quantity available. Grants are also available, particularly to help farming in difficult areas such as the uplands. However, in an attempt to reduce over-production, for example of dairy produce, the CAP has also imposed quotas on farmers.

Figure 3.2
Set-aside – paying farmers not to farm

Set-aside is another CAP scheme. This involves taking farmland out of agricultural use in order to reduce over-production. Participating farmers are given a set payment for each hectare within the scheme (it was £326/ha, with a maximum 5 per cent of land area allowed, in 1997/98). This is meant to compensate the income lost as a result of not cultivating that land. Although farmers can use the land for non-agricultural activities such as caravan sites and golf courses, it also provides an ideal opportunity to conserve wildlife. It allows natural regeneration of plant growth to take place and for land to become free from applications of pesticides and fertilisers. There is evidence that populations of some seed-eating birds may have benefited from set-aside. In many cases farmers have also received payments for planting trees on set-aside land through the Farm Woodland Management Scheme. It has to be said, however, that the scheme has not been popular with many farmers. They regard it as a waste of money, making farms untidy and encouraging the spread of weeds – blots on the landscape.

Recent attempts to reform the CAP have suggested an end to set-aside. In 1997 the area in the UK was reduced by half, bringing some 250 000ha back into intensive arable production. Another reform has been a shift away from guaranteed prices to a more market-led situation. There is also a move to channel CAP funds to support non-farming activities in rural areas, such as tourism and small businesses along with new packages aimed at preserving environmentally sensitive areas.

Review

2 Suggest three ways of reducing the EU's food surpluses. For each assess the pros and cons of your suggestion. Find out more about the EU's current practices of intervention buying, grants and quotas.

New techniques in agricultural production

In the EU the impact of government policies and the CAP has gone hand in hand with many major changes in agricultural production techniques. These include:

- using farmland more intensively
- using ever larger and more powerful machines such as combine harvesters
- greatly increasing the use of agro-chemicals – fertilisers and pesticides
- introducing new livestock-rearing methods, such as feeding cattle with animal protein, and battery farming of chickens
- using biotechnology to develop new breeds and varieties, including genetic engineering and cloning
- adopting new cropping patterns, such as sowing cereals in autumn rather than in spring
- increasing specialisation in production.

The consequences of these changes have been great – some beneficial, many highly controversial and others disastrous. Some examples of new biotechnology techniques are provided by the following case studies.

Case study: The mad-cow disease scare

'Mad-cow disease', or bovine spongiform encephalopathy (BSE) to give it its proper name, occurred in cattle during the 1980s and 1990s. Some 167 000 cases were reported in the UK between 1986 and 1997. The cause is thought to have been cattle-feed made from the recycled offal of sheep suffering from a rather similar disease called 'scrapie'. It had been thought that scrapie was specific to sheep, but it is now suspected of crossing the species divide to cattle through contaminated feed. From cattle, the disease seems now to have entered the human population through the consumption of meat and beef products (such as hamburgers) made from BSE-infected cattle. It is suspected that this may have given rise to a new strain of Creutzfeldt-Jakob disease (CJD) in people.

In 1996, the suspicion that the disease could cross species brought massive disruption to Britain's 40 000 dairy farmers and 70 000 beef farmers, and to associated industries such as abattoirs, meat-processing plants, hauliers and exporters. Consumer fears caused an initial 50 per cent reduction in beef sales in the UK. A global ban was imposed on the export of British beef and beef products such as tallow and gelatine. The EU insisted on the slaughter of all cattle over 30 months old and all other cattle thought to be at high risk of developing BSE.

Mad-cow disease has become a major political issue. There has been a huge compensation bill to be paid to the farmers, estimated at around £800 million, much of this coming from the EU. Currently, the number of human CJD victims is very small but, as the disease has a long incubation period, the final outcome is still unknown. It may take several years before the risk is entirely eliminated and the export ban fully lifted.

The BSE outbreak stresses the folly of violating natural laws in order to achieve ever greater efficiency, cheaper food and higher profits. Cattle are grass eaters. Giving them food containing protein made from other animals created an unnatural food chain and incurred new risks.

People have been selectively breeding animals and plants for many thousands of years in order to adapt and improve their productivity or to produce other desired characteristics. This is the traditional role of biotechnology, but since the 1960s new and more powerful techniques have been introduced to supplement older methods.

The latest methods of creating new hybrid varieties include tissue culture, recombinant DNA, embryo-transfer and cell-fusion techniques. Through genetic engineering, one of the more controversial forms of modern biotechnology, a gene with a particular trait in one organism can be directly inserted into another. Genetic structure can also be modified by radioactivity.

Research has been carried out into the potential of genetically modified or 'engineered' seeds and livestock. The aims have been to:

- increase resistance to pests and diseases
- improve tolerance to adverse conditions such as frost or drought
- increase crop and meat yields.

Case study: Genetically modified maize

In 1997 the world maize harvest was around 570 million tonnes, but each year a little less than 10 per cent of production is lost to attacks by the European corn-borer.

Recently, an American firm has developed a new strain of maize that is resistant to the pest. However, the EU is objecting to this breakthrough and has banned the import of the genetically modified seed. Why?

In this genetically modified maize an introduced gene produces a protein that is toxic to the corn-borer larvae, enabling the plant to resist attack. It is not toxic to other insects or animals. Incorporating the gene into the plant cells is a difficult process and it is necessary to check whether the new gene has been successfully added to the cell nuclei. To do this, two other 'marker' genes must be joined to the first. Thus, there are three new genes in the modified seed, not just one. This is where the EU objections lie.

One of the marker genes is resistant to a widely used antibiotic and the other is resistant to a frequently used group of herbicides. It is feared that the antibiotic-resistant gene might be passed on to bacteria in the digestive tract of livestock, thereby producing antibiotic-resistant bacteria. Similarly, the other gene could produce more herbicide-resistant varieties of plants. Some European scientists believe there could also be some risk to human health from these modified genes as they are passed on via the food chain. Yet another objection is that the genetically modified maize cannot easily be separated from normal maize. This means that it is not possible for consumers to tell whether or not they are purchasing food containing genetically modified material.

Case study: 'Dolly', the cloned sheep

Cloning is another example of modern biotechnology. Like people, individual sheep differ slightly from one another and possess their own characteristics such as temperament, growth rate and fertility rate. These characteristics are the result of very tiny differences in genetic make-up. Thus a particular breed of sheep will normally have a variety of common characteristics by which the breed is recognised. However, due to these minute genetic variations it cannot be guaranteed that every individual animal will be exactly the same.

Using the technique known as cloning, a sheep (named Dolly) was produced in 1996 that was absolutely identical to its mother in every respect. Clearly, the technique could be applied in other species of livestock. There could be major advantages in doing so, since there would be guaranteed growth rates, identical wool or hide characteristics and meat flavour.

There are, however, some major concerns. Some people object to cloning on moral grounds, seeing the issue as 'people playing God' or fearing that the technique could even be used to clone humans. Others fear the loss of genetic diversity, which could make an entire flock prone to attack by a new viral or bacterial infection or perhaps even a fungal disease.

Review

3 Read the three case studies (pages 25–27) on new techniques in agricultural production (biotechnology). For each, identify the key issue.

4 How far do you agree that 'progress in farming is inevitably a process of trial and error'? Justify your viewpoint.

SECTION D

The use of agro-chemicals

The use of chemicals is an everyday feature of modern agriculture. They include artificial fertilisers such as nitrates and phosphates, and a huge group of pesticides. The term 'pesticide' covers a multitude of different chemicals used to target the whole range of agricultural pests. Today, the farmer's chemical armoury includes herbicides, fungicides, insecticides, molluscicides and even nematicides.

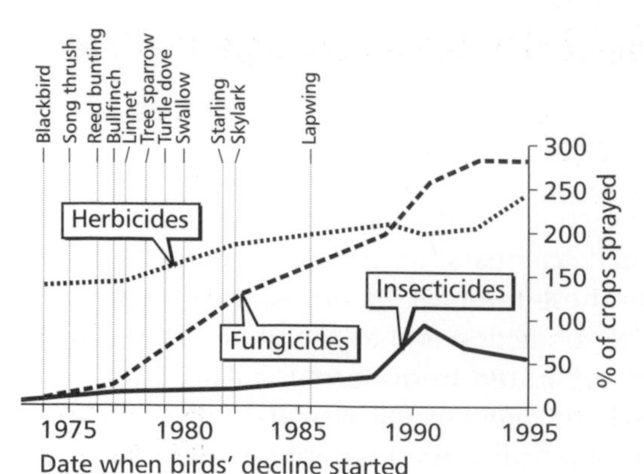

NB Herbicide and fungicide use exceeds 100 per cent because fields are sprayed more than once per season

Figure 3.3
How pesticides have hit birdlife

Herbicides are sprayed to remove weeds from crops, but if used carelessly the spray can drift into field margins, ditches and hedges, killing many more plants than the weeds that were originally targeted. This destroys the seeds and plant food of birds such as partridges, skylarks and linnets and of many butterflies and other insects. Owls and birds of prey are also deprived of food if, for example, field voles are destroyed.

Modern insecticides are much less persistent than the organo-chlorines that were widely used as seed dressings and as sheep dip during the 1950s and '60s. Persistent insecticides such as DDT and Dieldrin did immense damage to populations of birds of prey such as sparrowhawks, peregrine falcons and barn owls **(3.3)**. The chemicals accumulated in the fatty tissues of their bodies as these chemicals passed along the food chain:

toxic-dressed cereal seeds → stock dove → peregrine falcon

The decline of birds of prey provided an early warning that persistent insecticides affect non-target and often beneficial species. Farm operatives applying the insecticide sprays are particularly at risk but, via the food chain, so too are the consumers of the treated products from the residues on and within the food.

Although the more dangerous persistent chemicals are no longer used in the UK, they are still available and applied to crops in many developing countries. There is strong evidence that pesticide residues contaminate water supplies from surface runoff, leaching and spray drift. An example is provided by New Delhi, India's capital city, where very high levels of pesticide are being found in the water supplies. This has raised major concerns for the health of the city's 11 million people. Most of Delhi's drinking water is abstracted from a canal to the east of the city which has passed through many kilometres of farmland. The pesticides are leached from the farmland during the heavy monsoon rains and washed into wells and into the canal where, during the long, hot dry season, they are concentrated by evaporation.

Another problem with the use of pesticides is the rapid life-cycle of insects and many other pests. This means that if any individuals happen to be resistant to the chemicals, perhaps through some genetic variation, they will pass this resistance on to future generations. In this way, pests develop resistance to pesticides. The solutions are to:

- develop target-specific pesticides
- enforce safety measures in applying and handling pesticides so that non-target species are less likely to be affected
- develop less persistent chemicals with a shorter active life
- develop alternative pesticides that are used to overcome resistance
- introduce biological controls as alternatives to pesticides, e.g. ladybirds or hoverflies, the natural predators of aphids.

Review

5 a Outline the different uses of herbicides, fungicides and insecticides.

b Referring to **3.3**, which of these has had the most serious impact on wildlife?

Monoculture and specialisation in agriculture

The price-support mechanisms of the CAP have greatly encouraged the growth of such specialist crops as flax and oilseed rape, which frequently dominate huge areas of the countryside. But it is not only in Europe that this phenomenon is occurring.

Much of the food we consume in Europe is imported, often from developing countries. Attracted by the high prices we are able to pay, there is an increasing tendency for such countries to cater for the European market, with a consequent impact on tropical environments (soil depletion and erosion, deforestation, pollution, wildlife loss). There are also high environmental costs caused by unlimited food transport across the globe, which uses up huge amounts of energy resources. Many argue that this trade is not sustainable in the long term. It provides an example of how the ecological footprint (resources consumed per person) is far greater for those living in the industrial nations than those in developing countries (see **Chapter 1**).

Case study: Kenyan crop production for European consumption

Huge quantities of fruit, vegetables and flowers are grown in Kenya, especially by Dutch and British companies and by emigrant farmers. Many of these crops are of European origin and taste, and are not considered palatable by the local Kenyan people. Since air freight is relatively cheap these days, almost all of this produce is exported by plane to Europe. Its high quality makes it competitive with home-grown products – which in Europe incur high labour charges and, if they are grown under glass, expensive heating costs.

The area under such cultivation is increasing rapidly in Kenya, especially around Lake Naivasha, where major environmental problems are emerging. Crops grown in the tropics, particularly flowers, consume huge quantities of water, provided by irrigation taking water from the lake. As a result the level of the lake is falling rapidly, with a direct impact on wildlife species such as buffalo and hippopotamus. The widespread use of insecticides and herbicides, imported at high cost from overseas, is also an important factor in causing pollution. Some of the chemicals are so dangerous to farm labourers and wildlife that their use has been banned in Europe. Low wages are paid to the indigenous workforce, and the area of land available for growing food for local consumption has been severely reduced, leading to shortages, inflated prices and consequent hardship.

Review

6 a What do you understand by the term **monoculture?**

b Identify the advantages and disadvantages of monoculture for **i** the farmer and **ii** the environment.

7 Under the headings 'Pros' and 'Cons', list the benefits and costs of Kenya's production of food and flowers for the European market.

The changing agricultural landscape

In order to make the most efficient use of new farm machinery, farmers in the UK have found it necessary to enlarge their fields by removing hedgerows and trees, and filling in ponds and ditches **(3.4)**. It is estimated that since the Second World War, over 200 000km of hedgerows have been removed in Britain, a length almost sufficient to stretch five times around the Equator!

Figure 3.4 Change in the agricultural landscape in part of Hertfordshire, 1946 and 1985

Concern at hedgerow destruction centres on:

- consequent change to the chequerboard pattern of fields and hedges which for 200 years has characterised much of Britain's rural landscape
- loss of habitat for birds and other wildlife
- increased exposure of uncropped soils to erosion by wind and rain.

However, many land owners would argue in favour of such change, stressing that:

- small fields are uneconomic, since they make modern farm machinery difficult to manoeuvre
- maintenance of hedges is extremely costly
- hedges can harbour pests and diseases
- they take up land that would otherwise be used to produce food.

Just as hedgerows have been removed, so the marshes, fens and wet grasslands of river floodplains, coastal plains and deltas have been drained. These areas and the wild flora and fauna they support were dependent on seasonal flooding and grazing by livestock. When drained, the formerly wet areas are converted to arable land or land for more intensive animal stocking. The driving force behind these drainage programmes is the price support mechanism of the CAP, which favours the production of arable crops.

Case study: The draining of grazing marshes along the Thames estuary

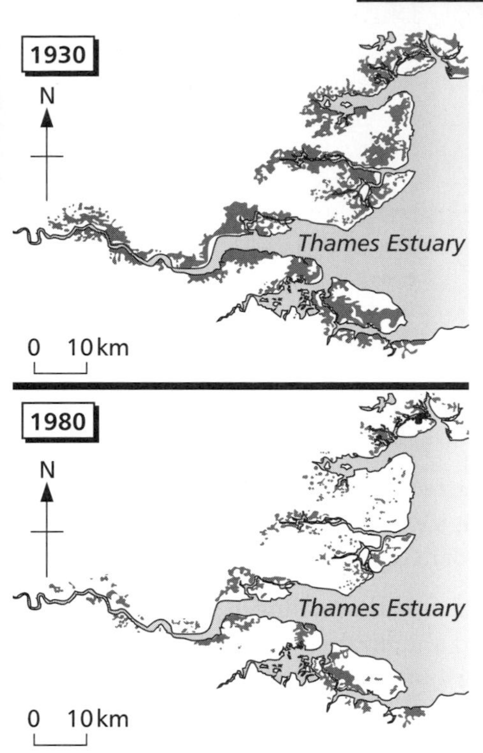

Figure 3.5 Decline in grazing marsh around the Thames estuary, 1930–80

Since the 1930s nearly two-thirds of the grazing marsh (about 28 000ha) has been destroyed in north Kent, in areas to the east of London and in parts of coastal Essex. A network of drainage ditches, sluices and pumps has been installed to minimise winter flooding and to lower the level of the water-table in summer. The extent of this drainage is shown by comparing the maps in **3.5**. Nearly 70 per cent of this area has been converted to arable land, but a substantial amount has been reclaimed for housing and industrial development.

Drainage of this kind is of particular concern to conservation organisations, which stress the value of such habitats to wading birds such as snipe, redshanks and lapwings that formerly bred there in summer, and for over-wintering flocks of geese and ducks.

In the UK the removal of wildlife habitats in farming areas has resulted in the sharp decline of many different wildlife species. These include:

- wild flowers, especially those that flourished in damp flower-rich meadows, e.g. the snake's head fritillary
- wild birds, especially seed-eaters, e.g. tree sparrow, linnet and corn bunting, the victims of a shortage of seeds in winter due to widespread adoption of winter-sown cereals; also wet-meadow species such as lapwings, snipe and redshanks due to drainage of wet grasslands
- butterflies and other insects, partly as a result of habitat loss and the removal of their wild food plants, but also due to the indiscriminate use of pesticides.

Case study: The decline in corncrakes

The corncrake provides a dramatic example of species decline. The numbers of this bird diminished rapidly during the 20th century along with a marked decrease in its geographical range. It was once a common hay-meadow bird, occurring right across the UK **(3.6)**. At the beginning of the 20th century corncrakes could be heard calling within a few kilometres of London. Today, the species is confined to a few islands in the Outer Hebrides in the far north and west of Scotland, and to western Ireland. Corncrakes nest on the ground in hayfields, but the widespread change from hay to silage means that the grass is cut much earlier, and this destroys both nests and young. Therefore it is only in crofting areas where traditional hay-making methods continue that a few corncrakes survive, but even these are threatened by problems of timing of the harvest and patterns of mowing. Perhaps more subsidies are required to encourage farmers to retain and practise traditional methods.

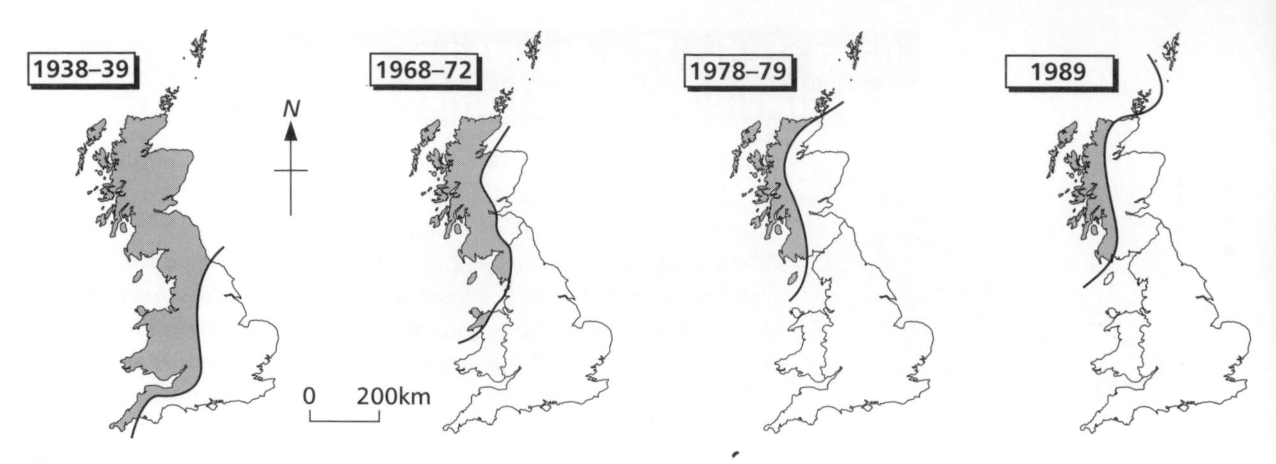

Figure 3.6 The contracting distribution of corncrakes, 1938–89

SECTION G

Soil degradation, erosion and conservation

Soil is a very thin layer lying on the surface of the lithosphere. It is an extremely fragile natural resource, but a crucial one since the ability of a farmer to grow crops is largely dependent on soil fertility.

Soil is a mixture of minerals and organic matter, arranged in layers or **horizons** as a result of both downward and upward movements of water through the soil profile. Plants play an essential role in soil formation but their growth is dependent on its water and nutrient content. Soil organisms such as springtails, earthworms, fungi and bacteria also play a vital role in the decay of dead organic material. They release the chemicals contained in the materials, recycling them for use by following generations. Thus whether they are growing crops or grazing livestock, farmers are exploiting soil as a natural resource. But soil is a resource that has taken thousands of years to form beneath vegetation as part of an ecosystem.

Most farmland has been used by many generations of people. The soil has been maintained, modified or enhanced by the addition of manure or other organic wastes, in order to maintain its moisture and nutrient content. However, many modern farming systems threaten the fertility of the soil and destroy its structure. It is possible that up to a third of the world's cultivated soils are currently experiencing erosion and loss of fertility.

Some of the problems caused by exploitation of soil as a natural resource were touched on in **Chapter 2**. Soils are vulnerable to erosion by such natural phenomena as wind and running water, but that vulnerability is often increased by human activities. These include:

- overstocking, which devastates the vegetation cover by overgrazing and trampling, and increases soil compaction
- compaction of soil by the use of heavy machinery, especially if the soil is wet
- erosion by wind and rain when cleared of its vegetation and left bare **(3.7)**
- removal of stored nutrients when crops are harvested, a particular risk in monoculture where the same crop is grown year after year

Review

8 The rural landscape of the UK has been changed dramatically since the Second World War by developments in farming and the Common Agricultural Policy. Identify six ways in which it has changed.

9 Compare the last two case studies (pages 31–32) and identify the causes of the changes shown.

- **laterisation** in tropical areas, where soils exposed to desiccation by hot sun develop a hard crust on the surface, of iron and aluminium sesquioxides
- increased soil salinity (**salinisation**) from irrigation, an all too common problem in hot arid areas such as the Middle East, India and parts of the USA
- channelling water into gullies by ploughing up and down slopes.

Figure 3.7 Soil erosion in Brazil following deforestation

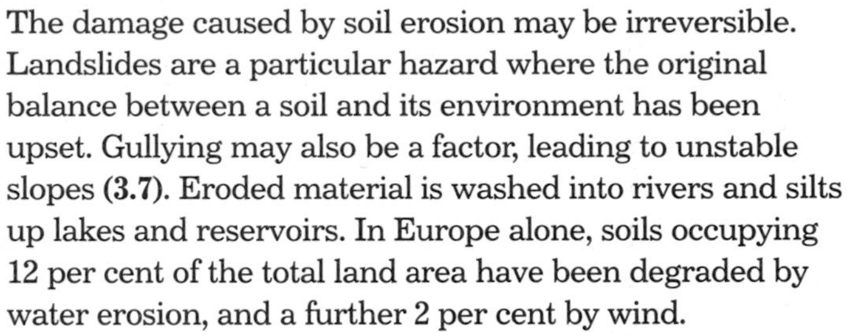

The damage caused by soil erosion may be irreversible. Landslides are a particular hazard where the original balance between a soil and its environment has been upset. Gullying may also be a factor, leading to unstable slopes **(3.7)**. Eroded material is washed into rivers and silts up lakes and reservoirs. In Europe alone, soils occupying 12 per cent of the total land area have been degraded by water erosion, and a further 2 per cent by wind.

Around 45 per cent of the land area of Spain has been affected by soil erosion of some kind. The problem is particularly severe in the Mediterranean area where the natural woodland and maquis scrub vegetation have been replaced by vineyards, and olive and almond groves. Some 9 million ha (18 per cent of the total area) is currently losing more than 50 tonnes of soil per year. This is the level at which erosion is regarded as a serious problem and is unsustainable.

Figure 3.8 Terraced rice fields in the Philippines

Wind erosion is a particular problem in more arid areas and was responsible for the 'dust bowl' of the USA's Great Plains in the 1930s. A combination of several years of high temperatures, drought, over-grazing and ploughing-up of the natural grass cover, made possible by the widespread use of tractors, exposed the soil to the ravages of strong winds. Even today, dust storms are still a problem in drier parts of the USA when strong winds are experienced.

Across the globe many techniques have been developed to counteract and reduce the adverse effects of soil erosion. It is, of course, most effective to protect soil from erosion in the first place. Removal of the vegetation cover is the most likely reason for erosion. Plant cover reduces raindrop and hail impact, and roots reduce surface runoff by permitting increased infiltration and binding soil particles together. It is therefore especially important to protect the surface, by means of a mulch or a crop, at times when conditions likely to cause erosion can be expected – during the wet season in those areas that receive seasonal rains, or when strong winds are most likely to occur.

Trees and hedges act as wind breaks and their removal exposes bare soils to wind erosion. An important technique in stabilising wind-blown sand dunes is to maintain the vegetation by fencing areas off to prevent trampling, and planting marram grass to cover bare areas. On slopes, vegetation cover can prevent gullying and make the removal of surface soil less likely. Steep slopes can also be protected from erosion by terracing, and this technique has been widely adopted in parts of China and the Philippines **(3.8)**. Another technique is to contour-plough slopes – that is, to plough along the line of the contour rather than up and down the slope. Strip cropping is rather similar – different types of crop are aligned along the contours, often using agro-forestry techniques with rows of trees or shrubs being interspersed with field crops.

Maintaining water in the soil is an important factor in retaining the vegetation cover, particularly in areas of seasonal rainfall, and can be achieved in several ways. The case study of an Indian village (pages 55–56) demonstrates some of these methods:

- the construction of small dams across streams
- the building of earth walls along field contours
- planting trees and protecting them from grazing animals.

All these techniques have proved effective in reducing runoff and allowing time for infiltration, thus retaining water where it falls.

Farmers adopting organic methods also claim that soil fertility is maintained and, indeed, enhanced. In essence, organic farming eliminates the use of artificial fertilisers and pesticides. It relies instead on crop rotation (involving manure crops such as clover which are ploughed back) and animal waste to maintain soil fertility. Soil pest problems are reduced. A thicker topsoil with more organic material and micro-organisms means improved rates of seed germination and good cropping.

Review

10 Make a list of:
a the major causes of soil erosion
b some suggested cures.

11 If organic farming is so good for the soil, why is it not more widely practised?

SECTION H

The Green Revolution and its consequences

The Green Revolution centres on increasing the production of food in developing countries such as Mexico and India. New high-yielding varieties (HYVs) of crops, including wheat, maize and rice, and imported animal breeds have been introduced. However, to make the most of HYVs, higher inputs are needed than for traditional indigenous types. It has therefore often been thought necessary by providers of foreign aid to introduce the new HYVs hand in hand with new technology – tractors and other machinery, weedkillers, chemical fertilisers, pesticides and veterinary products.

There is no doubt that many benefits have resulted from the Green Revolution. Food production has increased, with higher yields and more than one harvest each year. Crop damage by high winds and seasonal rains has been reduced. Living standards have improved for many people, especially those who have been able to afford the new technology and high inputs required.

However, many disadvantages have also been experienced. Indigenous crops and varieties of livestock have been displaced by the modern breeds and HYVs, and this is promoting monoculture. Genetic diversity is being lost, yet this is vital for maintaining pest and disease resistance in our major food crops, and to improve such aspects as flavour and resistance to drought. Famine and starvation have not been fully eliminated, especially in areas experiencing prolonged drought, perhaps as a result of long-term climate change. There are also problems of pollution and eutrophication resulting from their use. The over-use of irrigation in areas with a high evaporation rate has resulted in salinisation and waterlogging of soils.

Figure 3.9 A backlash of the Green Revolution – slums in Mumbai

In addition to physical problems, there are many social problems. Tenant farmers and small producers, too poor to afford the high costs of fertilisers and pesticides, are either kept in debt by the high interest charges made by moneylenders or they remain dependent on aid, much of which comes from overseas. Many farmers have been forced to give up. Thus the Green Revolution has accelerated the drift of people to the cities. Farm labourers are replaced by machines or suffer from the impact of drought. Ironically, many are displaced by major dam construction schemes (see the Narmada River project case study on page 54). In India, for example, up to 700 people a day arrive in the streets of Mumbai (formerly Bombay) from rural areas. They simply add to the shanty towns, slum development and poverty in which one-third of Mumbai's population already live **(3.9)**.

Solutions to the problems brought by the Green Revolution include:

- making better use of appropriate small-scale technology (such as that described in the Adgaon case study – see page 55)
- using drip irrigation rather than ditch or spray irrigation, as this requires less water and is less likely to induce salinisation or waterlogging
- using local organic manures such as compost and animal dung rather than chemical fertilisers
- ensuring proper crop rotations
- using hand labour and tools rather than costly machines.

Many other aspects of the Green Revolution are also being re-examined. Some of the high-tech HYV crops and imported animal breeds are now being questioned, as native breeds are more likely to survive and flourish in the low-input conditions of marginal farming environments. The knowledge of local farmers, traditionally more able to live sustainably in local micro-environments, has been undervalued. It is they who should be selecting, improving and using local plant and livestock diversity to suit the local conditions, building on traditional husbandry and land management.

In this chapter, we have seen that progress in agriculture has been made in both the developed and developing worlds. In all parts of the world, progress has been achieved at a cost both to the environment and biodiversity. In the developed world, progress has produced food surpluses, whilst in the developing world many people remain at or close to starvation level. The basic question must be: Is it possible to shift food from areas of surplus production to areas of deficit?

Enquiry

1 In the production of food, people are exploiting the natural resources of the lithosphere, hydrosphere, atmosphere and biosphere. Many techniques in agricultural production have a damaging impact on the environment and are not sustainable in the long term. For each of these four global spheres, suggest ways in which it may be damaged by food production.

2 Consider what is meant by the term **Green Revolution**. To what extent do you think the Green Revolution and other biotechnological techniques can help to bring about a greater degree of sustainability in food production?

3 What are the consequences of developments in agricultural production that require fewer people to work the land to grow large quantities of food:
a in less developed countries, and
b in more developed countries?

4 In small groups within your class, debate the issue:
'The problems of famine and starvation in the developing world cannot be solved simply by giving people who live there food surpluses from the developed world'.
You might find some of the literature available from aid charities such as Oxfam and ActionAid helpful to your discussion. Report the conclusions of the small group discussions to the whole class.

5 Visit your nearest large supermarket. Look at a sample of shelves displaying food products, e.g. the fruit and vegetable section. List the range of food products on display. Estimate the origins of these products and the proportions that have been grown in the UK; imported from Europe; imported from other temperate parts of the world; and imported from subtropical and tropical countries. Present your findings as bar graphs or pie charts.

6 Find out more about the EU's current practices of intervention buying, grants and quotas.
This information may be available from the reference sections of larger libraries, for example in publications from the EU and Ministry of Agriculture, Food and Fisheries (MAFF, or DAFFS in Scotland). Look, too, for reports in the more serious newspapers and such publications as *Farmers Weekly*.

Natural resources and fishing

SECTION A

Introduction

Fish are an important and invaluable source of food for the human population, being rich in protein and other nutritional essentials **(4.1)**. Fish stocks fluctuate, according to a number of environmental factors that are beyond human control. None the less, if stocks could be properly managed, fish could become an infinitely renewable natural resource.

Figure 4.1 Comparative nutritional values

Per 100g	Haddock	Herring	Prawns	Beef	Chicken	Lentils
Energy (Kcal/Kj)	81/345	190/791	76/321	179/748	230/952	381/1353
Protein (g)	19.0	17.8	17.6	19.6	17.6	23.8
Carbohydrates (g)	0	0	0	0	0	56.3
Fat (g)	0.6	13.2	0.6	11.2	17.7	1.3
Calcium (mg)	40	60	79	5	10	51
Iron (mg)	0.1	1.2	1.6	1.9	0.7	7.6
Niacin (mg)	4.4	4.1	0.5	4.8	6.0	2.0

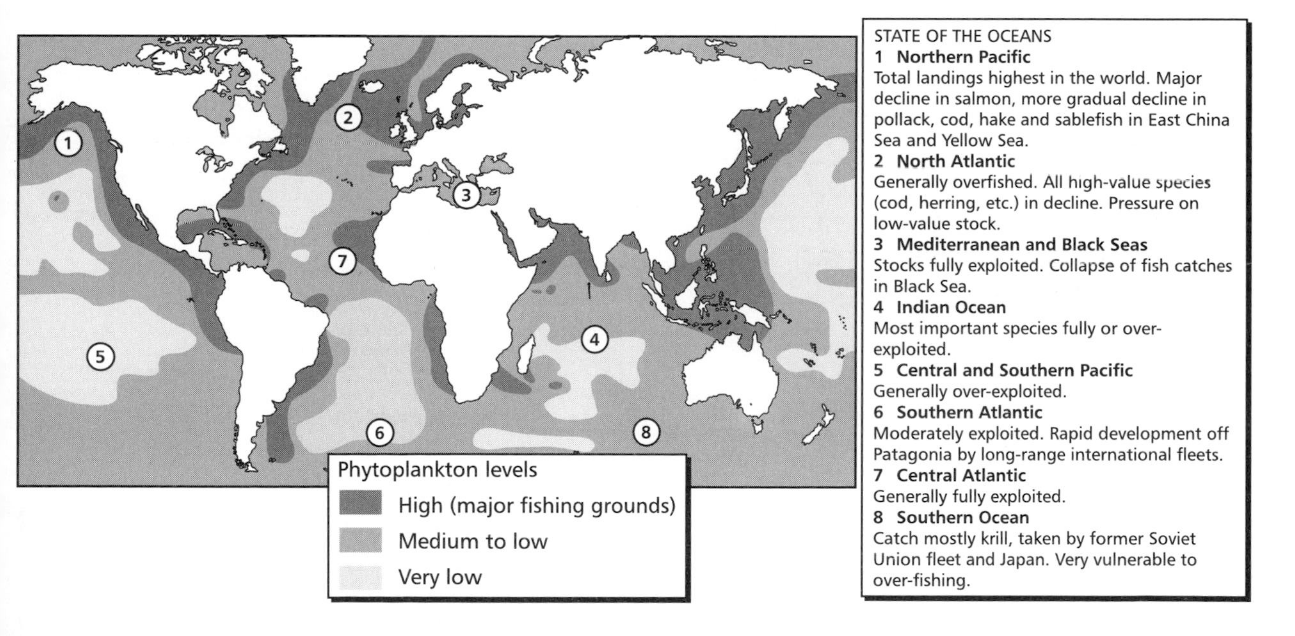

Figure 4.2 Where the fish are

Although the vast majority of the world's fish catches come from the seas and oceans, areas of fresh water also provide important fisheries in some landlocked areas. Three major types of sea area account for the greatest concentrations of the world's commercial fish stocks, often attracting fishing fleets from huge distances **(4.2)**:

- areas in which upwelling water from the ocean depths carries abundant nutrients to the surface, for example off the coast of north-west Africa and the south-east Pacific
- broad areas of continental shelf, such as around the British Isles and the Grand Banks off Newfoundland in the North Atlantic
- areas where tuna are plentiful.

Review

1 Assume that you are working for a large supermarket. You have been given the task of promoting the sale of fresh fish. What beneficial aspects of eating fish would you highlight?

2 Referring to **4.2**:
a Describe and explain the distribution of the world's major fishing grounds.
b Identify areas where low levels of phytoplankton occur and suggest possible reasons for this.

SECTION B

Modern fishing methods

Annual catches from the world's marine fisheries increased rapidly during the second half of the 20th century, rising from around 20 million tonnes in 1950 and levelling off in the early 1990s at an estimated 100 million tonnes per annum. A variety of economic, social and technological factors lie behind this massive increase:

Figure 4.3 The main methods used by today's fishing fleets

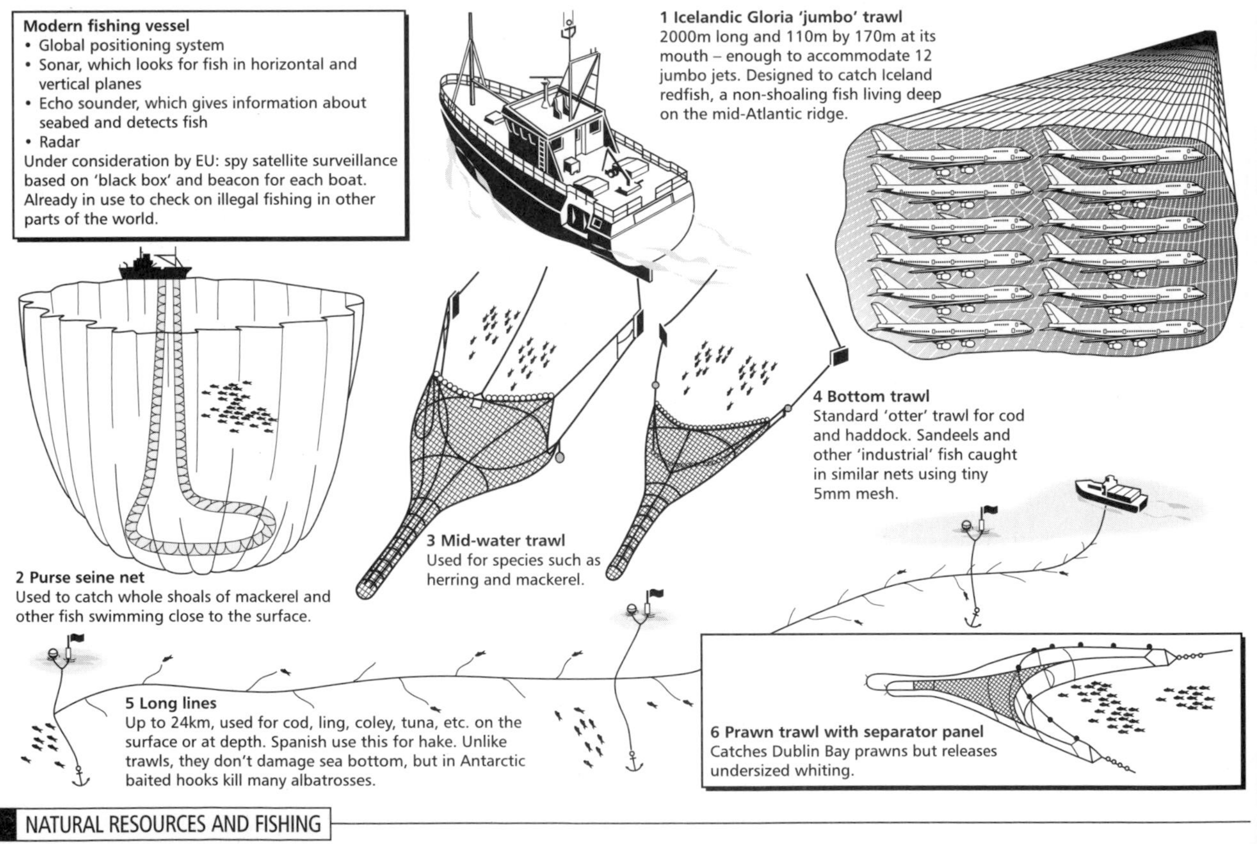

- the introduction of synthetic fibres and the mechanisation of hauling gear, which has led to larger and longer-lasting nets
- on-board freezing and processing, which has enabled fishing fleets to exploit fishing grounds far from their home ports
- better navigational aids and electronic devices, such as sonar and echo-sounders, which enable fish to be located more accurately
- new developments in satellites and computers, which help fishermen to locate shoals with pinpoint accuracy and enable them to anticipate and avoid unfavourable weather conditions.

Review

3 Make lists of the advantages and disadvantages of using modern technology in the fishing industry. Which of these lists appears to be the more convincing?

Some boats use nets so large that 12 jumbo jets would fit into their mouths **(4.3)**. Recently, fishermen in British Columbia caught their annual quota of herring (770 tonnes) in just eight minutes. The greatest increases in catches have occurred in various types of tuna; these rose by some 5 per cent per annum throughout the 1980s. However, catches of some lower-value species, such as the Alaskan pollack, have increased by as much as 10 per cent per annum.

SECTION C

Fish stocks

The global increase in marine fish catches tends to hide a number of causes for concern. The potential market for fish consumption continues to rise, but the annual catch worldwide has levelled off in recent years and is now beginning to fall. There is increasing evidence to suggest that some species have been seriously overfished. The result is that stocks of some species have plummeted. It is beginning to look as if world catches are close to, or may already exceed, the sustainable amount. To put it simply, there may be too many boats chasing too few fish.

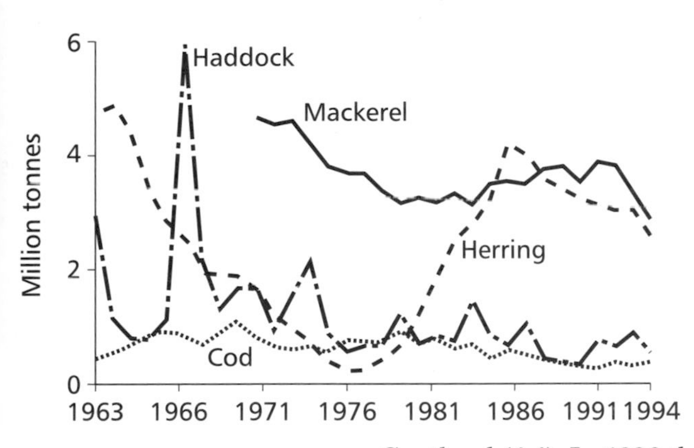

Figure 4.4 Declining fish stocks around the British Isles

In the North Atlantic, catches of cod, haddock, hake, herring and mackerel have all dropped rapidly due to over-exploitation. The North Atlantic cod was formerly one of the world's most important commercial fish stocks. However, in 1994 the International Council for the Exploitation of the Sea (ICES) recommended a moratorium on cod-fishing off Greenland, the Faeroes and the eastern Baltic, together with a major reduction in the catch off Iceland. Cod, haddock, plaice and sole are also described as being 'at historically low levels' in the North and Irish Seas and along the west coast of Scotland **(4.4)**. In 1996 the European Commission ordered a 50 per cent reduction in the North Sea herring catch to save falling stocks. In one year the British fishing fleet saw its annual herring quota cut from 64 000 tonnes to 22 000 tonnes. Researchers from the Scottish Office's marine laboratory claim that by the year 2000, cod could be uneconomic as a commercial species in the North Sea. Their research indicates that spawning stock has fallen from an estimated 350 000 tonnes in the late 1960s to under 75 000 tonnes in 1997. Even if fishing was drastically reduced, stocks would remain at risk. It is possible that the cod stock is about to collapse.

In the 1980s, the collapse of the Grand Banks cod fishery off Newfoundland caused the loss of an estimated 35 000 jobs. In 1992, the Canadian government imposed a local ban on fishing. However, it could not stop trawlers of other nationalities from fishing there. In 1997, the Grand Banks were opened again for cod fishing by Canadian boats, but many people fear that stocks are still too low and that the ban was lifted too soon.

Commercial fishing is not a selective process. Unwanted species and undersized specimens are inevitably caught, and this has also contributed to the decline in stocks. If too many young fish are caught in nets with a mesh that is too small, insufficient numbers are left to mature and to breed future generations. Current fishery regulations encourage the use of recommended minimum mesh sizes and the return to the sea of illegally small or unwanted species. In practice, huge quantities are killed in the nets and end up being dumped overboard and wasted. Globally, an incredible 27 million tonnes of dead, unwanted fish are dumped each year. That figure represents about a quarter of the retained catch.

Case study: The Shetland sandeel crisis

In spite of their small size, sandeels have a significant commercial value as a source of fish oil. They are also converted to fishmeal for use as fertiliser, feed for chickens and other livestock, food for fish farming and for mink rearing. In Denmark an electricity power station is fuelled by burning sandeels.

Sandeels are found in large shoals in the inshore waters around the Shetland Isles, and are easily caught. As sandeels are plankton-feeders, they are close to the bottom of the food chain, preyed on by many higher marine animals, namely larger fish and seabirds such as auks and terns. Thus modern industrial fishing methods have seriously reduced the main food source of Shetland's internationally important seabird colonies.

Catches of sandeels in the waters off Shetland showed a rapid growth from some 8000 tonnes in 1974 to a peak of 52 600 tonnes in 1982. Sharp declines in catches were then experienced, leading to closure of the fishery in 1991.

For six years in succession, from 1984 to 1989, the Shetland population of Arctic terns failed to raise any young. Research showed that their failure was due to too few sandeels and the consequent starvation of chicks. Kittiwakes, puffins and other internationally important seabirds similarly failed to breed.

There is still much debate over the cause of the sudden decline in sandeels. Was it a natural decline caused by some variation in environmental conditions, or was it a result of overfishing? Conservation organisations argue that if the long-term effects of any commercial activity are not known, then the 'precautionary principle' should be adopted to avoid potential disaster. In the case of the Shetland sandeel fishery, conservationists claim that the closure of the fishery should continue until more is understood about its management so that the safety of internationally important wildlife populations can be guaranteed. However, despite their strong protests, the fishery was officially re-opened in 1995.

Review

4 Taking the viewpoint of a wildlife conservationist, write a letter to a national newspaper putting forward the case for adopting the 'precautionary principle' by imposing a ban on commercial fishing for sandeels.

SECTION D

International disputes

International disagreements about whaling have been much publicised, with Japan and Norway defying conservationist concerns about dwindling stocks (**4.5**). However, this is just one of many disputes creating friction between nations.

Sanctuary for whales may allow more kills

PROPOSALS for a global whale sanctuary will come before the International Whaling Commission at its annual meeting in Bournemouth today. But some governments and conservationists fear that it may lead to more whales being killed.

The plan, which is believed to be supported by most nations, aims to stop countries such as Japan and Norway flouting the rules and whaling in international waters. In return for supporting the sanctuary, they will be given the right to catch whales commercially in their own waters up to 200 miles offshore.

Japan and Norway, and perhaps in the future other nations, could legally catch whales migrating through their coastal waters. Several species could be over-exploited. They included minke whales, Bryde's whales, fin whales and humpbacks.

Vassili Papastavrou of the International Fund for Animal Welfare said: 'There is a general move away from global international treaties in respect to the sea. The move now is to give national governments or regional groupings responsibilities. But this would be a disaster for whales as they are a highly migratory species.'

Elliot Morley, a junior Agriculture Minister, said yesterday that if a global sanctuary were approved, Britain would not rule out backing the resumption of small-scale, commercial coastal whaling. 'We will have to see exactly what it means in terms of the number of whales that would be at threat from coastal whaling. There are issues of cruelty too.'

Few countries and conservation groups disagree that action is needed. More than ten years ago, the International Whaling Commission voted overwhelmingly for a moratorium on whaling. But the number of animals killed has continued to grow.

Japan, which carries out so-called scientific whaling, officially caught 330 minke whales in 1993, which has now grown to about 540. The whales are killed in the Antarctic and Pacific and much of the meat ends up, not in laboratories, but on the tables of Tokyo restaurants.

Norway, which has exempted itself from the moratorium, killed some 226 minkes in 1993 but the latest catch is just over 500. Scientists and investigators also claim that through DNA testing they have found meat from such species as the blue whale on sale in Japanese markets.

The Times, 29 September 1997

Figure 4.5 The whaling debate continues

Early in 1995, a major international conflict broke out between Canada and Spain, caused by overfishing and the global decline of fish stocks. Spanish trawlermen and Canadian coastguards were involved in a series of running battles off the Newfoundland coast. On 9 March, a Spanish trawler that had been fishing for halibut (called turbot in Canada) was arrested outside Canada's 200-mile coastal limit, accused of using nets with a mesh smaller than the minimum size set by the North Atlantic Fishery Organisation.

Spain is in third place, after Japan and Korea, in the league table of world fish consumption. It has a fishing fleet of 19 000 vessels, the largest in the EU. In 1994, Spanish trawlers caught some 40 000 tonnes of Newfoundland fish, compared with only 4000 tonnes taken by local fishermen. To settle the dispute, the EU has suggested restricting the Spanish quota for Newfoundland fish to just 8000 tonnes per annum, with the local Newfoundland fishermen's quota raised to 10 000 tonnes. However, the Spanish claim that the fishing communities in north-west Spain would be devastated by such a huge reduction.

These fishing disputes in the north-west Atlantic coincided with a United Nations (UN) conference that was trying to find acceptable solutions to the fish-stock crisis. The UN estimates that 70 per cent of the world's

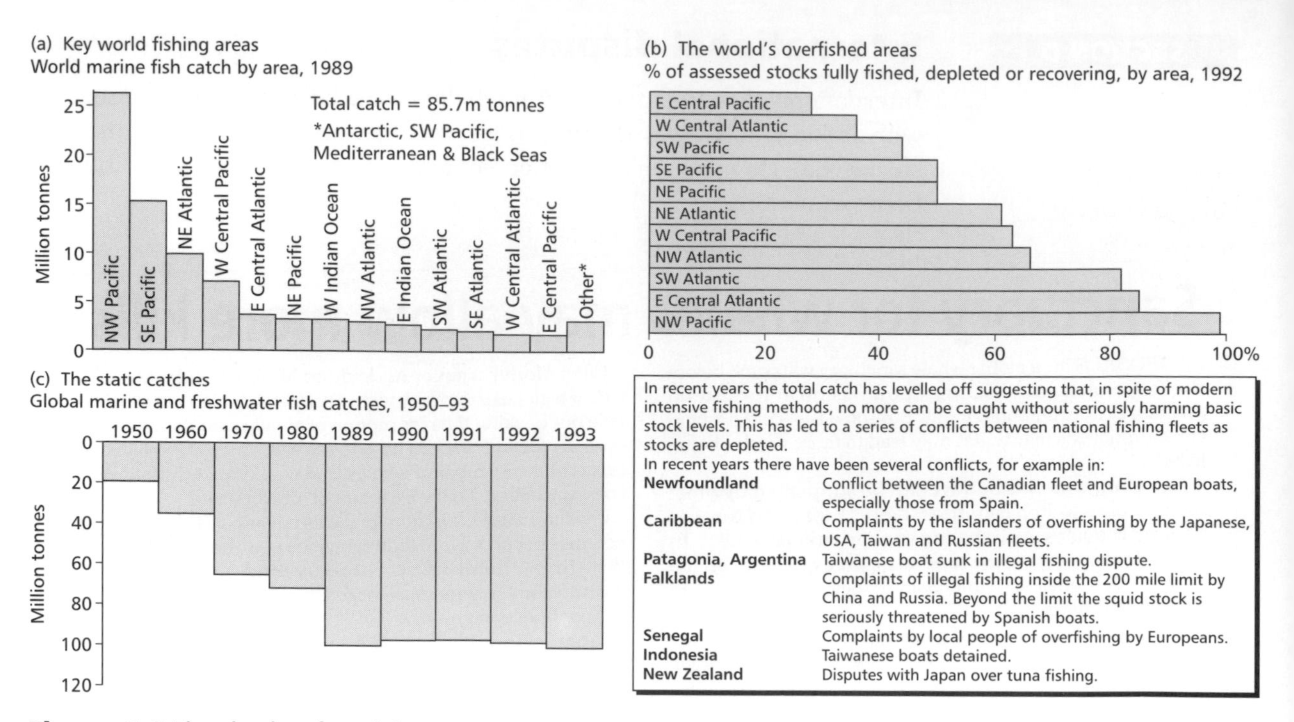

Figure 4.6 The plunder of the seven seas

fisheries are static or in decline, and believes that the trawling fleets have the capacity to wipe out all the remaining stocks in the next few years. Environmental organisations point out that there is no international body for the regulation of fish stocks and to manage the fisheries in a sustainable way.

There is also turmoil among the fishing fleets of the EU. There are calls for decommissioning 40 per cent of the fishing fleet. There are disputes, particularly between the UK and Spain, over rights to fish in British waters, and tight quotas have been imposed. Nevertheless, there are accusations that some countries are ignoring these quotas. Calls to put a stop to 'quota hopping' became a major issue during the 1997 General Election campaign in the UK. The quota system allows fishermen to sell their licences. Many British fishing boats have sold theirs to Spanish, Dutch and Danish boats. These foreign boats are thereby allowed to operate in British waters under a 'flag of convenience'. 'Quota hopping' is a means by which some nations are able to claim that they have reduced their fleet sizes in line with EU directives without in fact having done so.

Possible ways of reducing overfishing and conserving stocks include:

- establishment of an internationally recognised regulatory body
- use of satellites to track and monitor the activities of trawler fleets
- the compulsory fitting of transponders (identification devices) to all commercial fishing vessels
- establishment of 'no fishing zones' in major breeding areas
- support for EU attempts to reduce the total catch by decommissioning boats and compensating displaced owners
- strict policing of quotas and enforcement of minimum net-mesh sizes by an international inspectorate and through improved port-landing checks

- eliminating 'discard at sea' by introducing new technical measures to minimise the catching of undersized and non-target fish – boats required to land the whole-catch as a check.

Review

5 Read the newspaper extract (**4.5**).
   a Why do you think that, in spite of international opposition, Norway and Japan will continue to kill whales?
   b Do you think their case can be justified?
   c Are there any advantages to be gained by allowing the resumption of coastal whaling on a small scale?

6 What arguments would you make in response to the Spanish government's claim that any further reduction in fishing quotas will have a serious effect on its fishing communities?

7 Using the information in **4.6**, what is the correlation between overfishing and the world's most important fishing areas?

8 Several ways of reducing overfishing are outlined above. Rank these in terms of **a** their feasibility and **b** their likely effectiveness. Select the method that you think is most likely to be effective in solving the problem, and make out a reasoned case for its option internationally.

SECTION E

Aquaculture

With 70 per cent of global wild fish stocks either depleted or near collapse, great increases in fish farming **(aquaculture)** can be expected in the near future. The world's aquaculture industry already accounts for around 20 per cent of the overall fish harvest. At present, 95 per cent are freshwater species, but the farming of saltwater species is developing rapidly. Fish farming for such species as trout, salmon, crustacea and shellfish (including oysters and mussels) has become an economic activity in many parts of the world. While trout need freshwater ponds, salmon and shellfish are most frequently farmed by anchoring huge floating cages in sheltered waters, for example in the rias and fiords of Ireland, Scotland, Norway and Chile **(4.7)**.

Figure 4.7 Salmon farm cages in a sheltered stretch of coastal water

Salmon farming, particularly in northern Europe and Chile, has greatly increased in recent years. During the 1970s, salmon production was around 400 000 tonnes; this increased to 600 000 tonnes in 1980, reaching more than 1 million tonnes in 1990. Salmon prices have declined markedly as a result, and farmed salmon is now cheaper than cod. In 1994, some 60 000 tonnes of farmed salmon were consumed in the UK alone. Norway is now the major salmon-farming country in Europe, producing 292 000 tonnes in 1996 compared with Scotland's 83 000 tonnes.

A big problem with farming most high-value species is their carnivorous nature. They must be fed on fishmeal – high-value fish are fed on lower-priced fish, such as sandeels, taken from the wild. Research is going on to find a farmable herbivorous (plant-eating) white fish that appeals to the Western palate. If this is successful, the costs of farmed fish to the environment, and to the consumer, can be greatly reduced.

Shrimps and prawns are another important group, with a total catch from all sources (wild and farmed stocks) more than doubling from 1.1 million tonnes in 1980 to nearly 2.5 million tonnes by 1990. China accounted for the most dramatic increases in shrimp production, with a fivefold rise in 20 years, to reach 20 per cent of the world's production in 1990. Aquaculture now accounts for one-third of China's shrimp production. However, since 1987 Thailand has been the world's largest exporter of farmed shrimp. During the 1980s, many Thai farmers rushed to get in on the shrimp-farming boom, destroying many of the country's mangrove swamps in the process. The same thing has happened in India.

The UN Food and Agriculture Organisation sounds a note of caution on aquaculture: 'The challenge is formidable. Proper planning, environmental considerations, proper systems management and disease control will have to play a more important role than at present if crashes in production are to be avoided.'

Fish farming can cause environmental problems:

- scenic views spoiled by ugly and obtrusive cages and other equipment
- the attraction of predators such as cormorants and seals, and parasites such as sea lice which may need to be controlled by chemical pesticides
- severe pollution from the concentration of droppings and uneaten food in enclosed waters
- introduction of alien species to an area, which may compete with native species
- the destruction of habitats, such as mangrove and other wetlands, by the creation of fish ponds.

Case study: The Blue Revolution

Traditionally, small-scale Indian rice farmers in such states as Kerala have produced prawns for their own consumption or for local markets, by cultivating them in paddy fields after the harvest of the rice crop. Both inputs and yields were small, and after the harvest the top saline soil was heaped up so that it was leached of salts by the next season's monsoon rains. Salt-resistant rice was then planted and yields were good as the soil had been enriched by waste from the prawns.

During the 1990s India, along with other Asian countries such as Thailand, China and Taiwan, has been in the forefront of what has been called the **Blue Revolution** – the farming of shrimps and prawns for export. Intensive farming methods are used involving purpose-dug ponds flushed with saline water and provided with artificial aeration. They make heavy use of fertilisers, hormones, antibiotics and pelletised fishmeal, all with the aim of producing bigger and fatter prawns in the shortest possible time (four months from egg to harvest). High stocking densities are employed in order to maximise production.

Figure 4.8
A shrimp pond in Thailand

Serious problems have been created by the Blue Revolution. There have been outbreaks of disease caused by a mysterious virus; the disease has proved lethal. The discharge of untreated toxic effluent has caused water pollution and the destruction of coastal mangroves. This has triggered a number of knock-on effects, including the destruction of wild fish stocks and other marine life, thereby hitting the livelihood of local fishermen. Aquaculture has also had the effect of increasing levels of salinity in wells and seriously degrading formerly fertile agricultural land adjacent to the ponds.

The Indian Supreme Court has recently introduced an order banning the establishment of aquaculture farms within 500 metres of high-tide levels along India's coast. Existing farms that do not comply have been shut down and compensation paid to those thrown out of work as a result. This has introduced two principles which many regard as essential to sustainable environmental management:

1 The 'precautionary principle' which holds that the health of ecosystems and wild species must be given priority; if there is any doubt, then the potentially damaging action must be avoided.
2 The 'polluter-pays principle', by which people or businesses bear the costs of measures to reduce or clear any pollution they have created.

In conclusion, it needs to be emphasised that fish are an important source of food. But the resource is not being exploited in a sustainable way. Drastic and immediate action is needed if fish stocks are to be conserved even at their present depleted levels. On the face of it, increased aquaculture looks to offer a sensible way forward. If it is to fulfil this promise then a whole range of environmental problems will have to be resolved.

Enquiry

1 Set out the pros and cons of aquaculture as a means of overcoming the decline in global stocks of wild fish.

2 Organise a class debate on the motion: 'This house believes that as long as national interests are put first, there can be little hope of conserving global fish stocks.' You will need proposers and seconders to argue the cases for and against the motion.

CHAPTER

5

The exploitation and management of water resources

SECTION A

Why do we need water?

Clean, fresh water is a natural, renewable resource on which all living things depend. We need reliable water supplies in our homes for drinking, cooking, washing, cleaning and watering the garden. Every person in England and Wales uses, on average, some 160 litres of water every day **(5.1)**. Over the last 30 years domestic consumption has increased by 70 per cent. The volume continues to rise and it is predicted that by 2021 we will each use 190 litres per head per day. This should be contrasted with the average 15 litres of water per day used by a family living in the slums of Mumbai, India.

Figure 5.1 The domestic uses of water in the UK

	%
Car washing, dripping taps and leakage	32.5
WC flushing and waste disposal	32.0
Bathing and showering	17.0
Washing machines	12.0
Gardening and outside	3.0
Drinking and cooking	2.5

In the UK we take it for granted that clean water will flow every time we turn on a tap. We assume it will be instantly available to us at all times. Imagine what things would be like if the supply was cut off or strictly rationed! We tend to think of water as a 'free' commodity, but in fact each household has to pay for it through their water rates or, increasingly, via a bill for the amount used as recorded by a meter.

The quantity of water used each day in the homes of England and Wales alone amounts to a colossal 16 billion litres – approximately half of the total daily amount abstracted from both surface and groundwater sources. The other half is used on our behalf by a huge variety of services and industries **(5.2 and 5.4)**. These include hospitals, sports facilities and factories, particularly those involved in heavy manufacturing. Huge amounts of water are also used during the generation of electricity, when it is needed for cooling purposes in both thermal and nuclear power stations. Although the water abstracted for cooling purposes is usually returned to a water-course, the increased water temperatures can have a marked impact on the environment. Pollution hazards are increased and the biological oxygen demand (BOD) is raised, causing problems to fish and other wildlife.

Figure 5.2 Some typical quantities of water used in manufacturing

Goods manufactured	Amount of water used (litres)
1 average-sized motor car	30 000
1 tonne of steel	4545
1 tonne of ready-mixed concrete	455
0.5 litres of beer	4.5

Review

1 Why has per capita water consumption risen so much over the last 30 years?

2 Find out from your regional water company how it proposes to reduce levels of water consumption.

Water is also very important in food production, which uses about 2 per cent of the total volume abstracted. In recent decades, agricultural demands have grown dramatically and they are predicted to rise still further. In the drier areas of the UK, spray irrigation of crops is a major user. Fish farming (aquaculture) also requires large amounts. Yet another demand is from recreation, where angling, sailing, water-skiing, wind surfing and other sports require large areas of surface water, preferably in attractive surroundings.

SECTION B

Where does our water come from?

Water is a natural resource provided by the hydrosphere. We tend to use water as if it were unlimited, but in reality supplies are finite and unevenly distributed. Ongoing but limited supplies are available for abstraction from the hydrological cycle **(5.3)**. Total water abstraction in England and Wales currently amounts to 32 billion litres per day. This figure is expected to rise to some 40 billion litres per day by the year 2000.

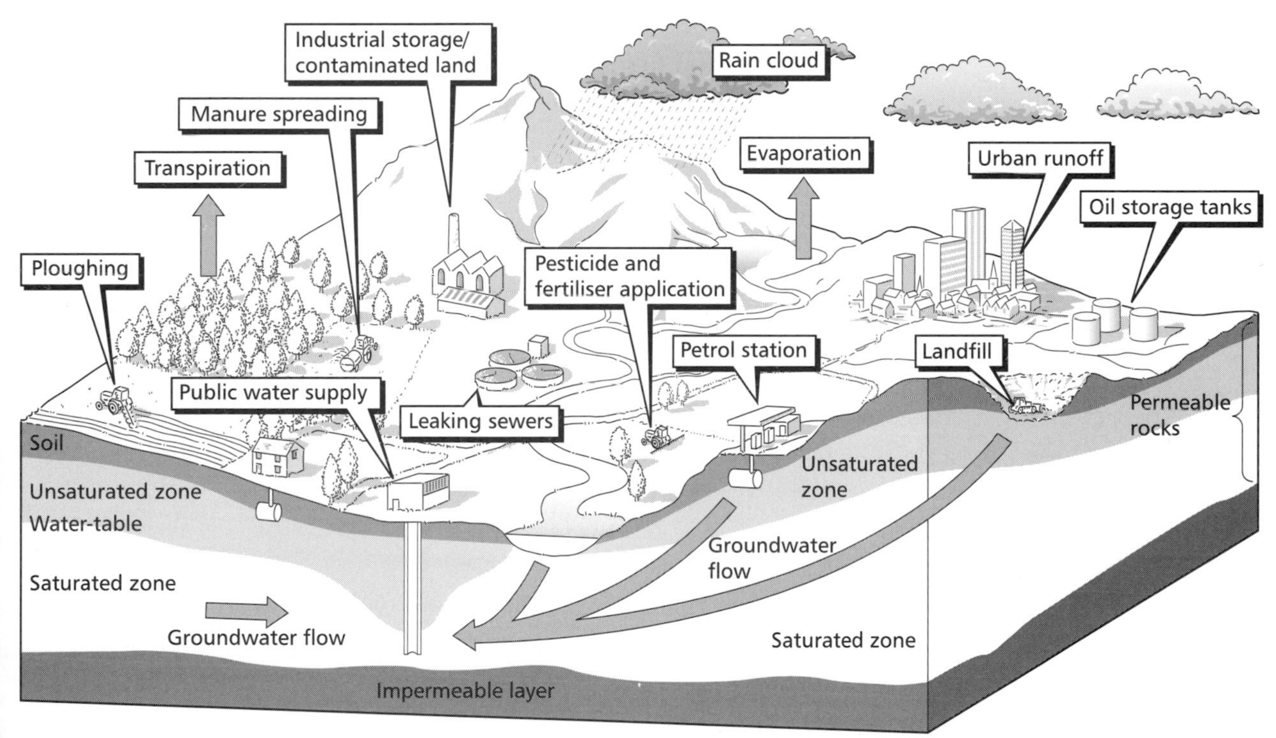

Figure 5.3 The hydrological cycle and some sources of water contamination

In Britain the Environment Agency monitors water quality and is responsible for flood control, while the recently privatised water companies provide our homes and industry with supplies. They:

- collect and store water
- treat and purify supplies
- provide amenities for water-based recreation
- prevent pollution of rivers
- dispose of industrial and domestic waste water
- conserve wildlife and fisheries.

The water companies obtain their supplies from two main stages of the hydrological cycle **(5.3** and **5.4)**:

1. From surface water – that is, the precipitation that remains on the surface, which is abstracted from rivers, lakes and reservoirs. Recreational activities increasingly demand access to areas of fresh water. Fortunately, reservoirs provide attractive scenery and are ideal locations for such activities as angling, sailing, water-skiing. Many forms of wildlife depend on reservoirs too.
2. From groundwater – that is, precipitation that has percolated into the soil and underlying rocks and which is abstracted by pumping. Porous rocks such as chalk, limestone and sandstone are aquifers, absorbing water like a sponge. About 25 per cent of the total UK supply is pumped from aquifers.

Figure 5.4 Sources and uses of water abstraction in England and Wales (ml/day)

Use	Surface	Ground	Total
Domestic supply	11 613	5038	16 651
Industry	1485	681	2166
Mineral washing	52	142	194
Spray irrigation	83	80	163
Fish farming	3533	284	3817
Electricity	8961	35	8096
Other	133	183	316
TOTAL	25 860	6443	32 303

Review

3 With reference to **5.3**, identify the main points in the hydrological cycle at which water supplies are extracted.

4 a Your task is to represent the data in **5.4** as appropriate graphs. For each of the three columns you will need to consider the range of the data so that you can select the most appropriate technique (for example bar graph, pie chart or proportional symbols), and a suitable scale.

b To what extent do uses differ in terms of their sources of water?

5 a In what types of rock do aquifers occur?

b Referring to an atlas with a geological map of the British Isles, trace the outline and plot the distribution of these rocks in England and Wales.

c Plot the major cities on the same map.

d What conclusions do you draw about the relationship between cities and aquifers?

SECTION C

The effects of drought

The huge quantities of water used in the UK are of concern to both suppliers and consumers. There is strong evidence that water abstraction is damaging the environment and wildlife. The recent hot, dry summers followed by equally dry winters have had a more serious effect than would have been the case in the past.

Figure 5.5 Ladybower Reservoir in the Pennines, during a drought

Under normal conditions, the lack of rainfall in exceptionally dry years is offset by seepage from water stored in natural aquifers and wetlands (marshlands, fens and peat bogs) which are formed where the water-table is at or close to the surface. However, the artificial drainage of wetlands and the lowering of water-tables by pumping has removed this emergency reserve which, in the past, kept streams and rivers flowing throughout the year.

Rivers have been straightened and canalised in order to control flooding. This too has reduced the amount of water available to soak into the ground. Water is pumped directly from rivers, particularly for spray irrigation of crops, and this has reduced their flow even further. Nearly 100 rivers in Britain have dried up or had their flow reduced to a mere trickle. This damage has also had a disastrous effect on fish and other wildlife.

Case study: Examples of disruption to eco-systems caused by abstraction and drought

1 **Hundleshope Burn** is one of the turbulent, oxygen-rich headwaters of the River Tweed. Migratory fish such as salmon and sea trout spawn in streams like this which rise in the mountains. However, these species have been prevented from swimming upstream to reach the headwaters, by reduced flows, low dissolved-oxygen levels and an increased

concentration of pollutants in the lower course. Ironically, in this case, much of the abstraction has been to supply water for fish farming.

2 The **River Ver** in Hertfordshire was until recently a typical chalk stream, but the groundwater in the chalk aquifer has been excessively pumped in order to provide Hertfordshire's growing urban communities with a domestic water supply. This pumping has caused the river's feeder springs to fail. A 10km stretch of the Ver has ceased to flow since 1995, while other sections have become shallow, sluggish and choked with weed.

   The surrounding water-meadows have also dried out. The result is that redshank and snipe have been lost. These wading birds need soft ground kept moist by a high water-table in order to probe for worms and similar food items. In many parts of Britain, drainage and lower water-tables have reduced the numbers of these birds by as much as 70 per cent.

3 **Redgrave and Lopham Fens**, located on the Norfolk/Suffolk border, are home to the great raft spider. This is Britain's largest and rarest spider, an inhabitant of fenland pools. It is found at only two locations in the UK; the population at Redgrave and Lopham Fens is probably no larger than 100. The spider feeds on insects and small fish. Groundwater abstraction from a nearby borehole has caused a huge drop in the water-table in the underlying chalk aquifer, so this highly endangered species is now threatened with extinction. The threat has been exacerbated since 1995 by drought. Water levels in the ponds have fallen by more than 25cm.

   Conservationists have now negotiated a solution to the problem with the Essex and Suffolk Water Company. The scheme involves the creation of a new, more distant borehole and the pumping of water into a series of small ponds that are being managed especially for the great raft spider. During the drought in 1997, the water company expected to pump as much as 50 million litres of water to maintain water levels high enough for the spider's survival – enough water to meet the requirements of over 2000 people for six months.

4 The **Kennet**, a tributary of the Thames, was once one of Britain's best trout-fishing rivers. Today it is suffering from drought and the effects of over-abstraction. One reason for the increased abstraction is the fact that the Kennet is within the M4 corridor, the scene of much urban development in recent decades, and where there is a promise of more to come. From its source near Avebury in Wiltshire to its confluence with the Thames at Reading, the Kennet's flow has been reduced and its velocity lost. Normal plant life has died as the river has become clogged with algae. This algae blooms as a result of nitrates and phosphates being washed into the river from adjacent farmland.

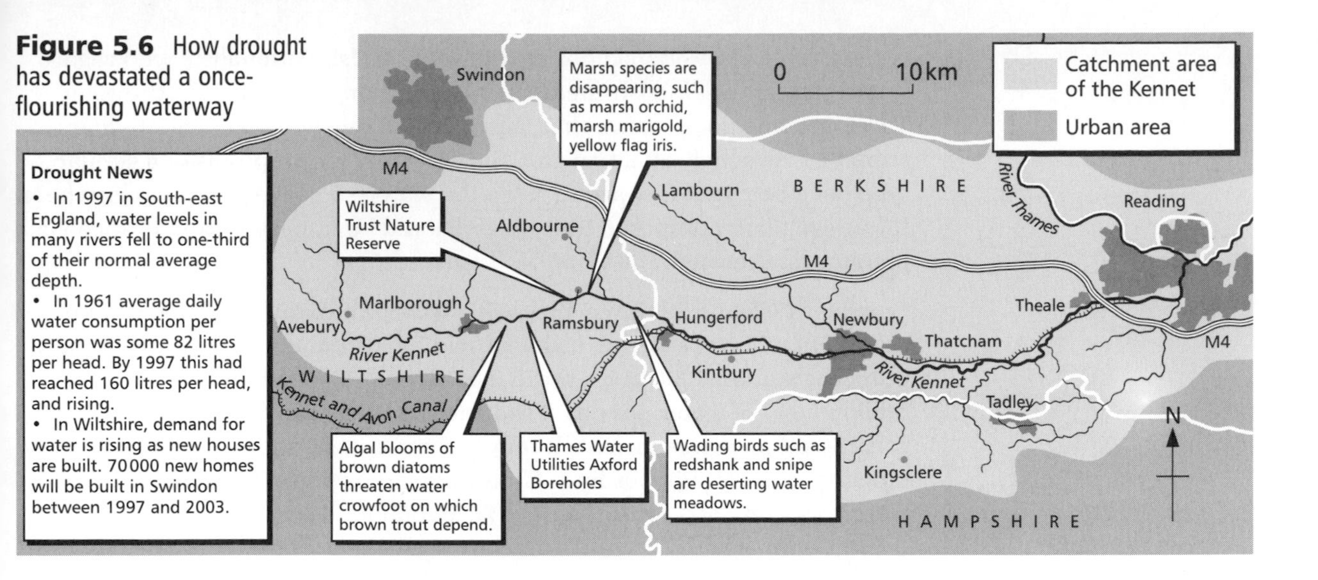

Figure 5.6 How drought has devastated a once-flourishing waterway

Review

6 Discuss the statement: 'Drought is a natural hazard aggravated by people'.

7 Suggest five ways in which the plight of the River Kennet and upper Thames might be resolved.

SECTION D

Solving the water crisis

The water companies claim that six new reservoirs are needed in south-east England alone to ensure sufficient water supplies to meet the increased demands of the 21st century. This predicted increase in demand is made even more likely by the effects of global warming and more single-person households. How can the crisis be resolved?

Repairing leaks It is estimated that a total of some 5000 million litres of water are wasted every day. This amounts to 16 per cent of all the water abstracted from the environment. One litre in every six is being lost before it can be delivered to the customer. In the area supplied by Thames Water plc, the situation is even worse, with more than 30 per cent lost by leakage from underground pipes. Urgent efforts are being made to repair these leaking pipes and to reduce the incidence of burst water-mains. For example, computer-controlled flow systems are being installed which automatically decrease water pressures during the night and other periods of low demand.

Water transfer Another problem for the UK's water supplies is that demand is greatest in the areas that receive the least rainfall. Since the 1890s, most of Birmingham's water has been transported via a 150km pipeline from the Elan Valley reservoir in mid-Wales – an area of high rainfall. This scheme supplies about 75 million litres of water a day to Severn Trent Water plc. There is political argument about this export of water, with considerable opposition coming from some Welsh nationalists who regard it as a case of the English 'stealing' Welsh water. None the less, the Elan Valley scheme does ensure that Birmingham receives an adequate daily supply of very high-quality water. Several transfer proposals of a similar type have been put forward to solve the water-shortage problem elsewhere. It has even been proposed that water should be imported from France via a pipeline laid through the Channel Tunnel.

Between 1995 and 1997, the Yorkshire Water company alone spent more than £170 million repairing leaks, providing 100km of pipeline and 10 new pumping stations. Although these measures should supply an extra 240 million litres of water per day if they are needed, supplies are still considered to be insufficient. It may prove necessary to construct a new pipeline to carry supplies from Kielder reservoir in Northumberland to West Yorkshire, at a further cost of £220 million.

A national water grid This proposal calls for the construction of new reservoirs in water-surplus areas in the north and west of the UK and the transfer of supplies to areas of water deficit in the south and east, via a national grid system. This would require the very costly construction of a large network of long, high-capacity pipelines.

A less costly option has been suggested, whereby water would be moved from areas of water surplus via the existing network of canals and rivers, which would become a kind of open pipeline system. Pumping stations would be strategically located to lift water across watersheds from one catchment area to another. However, pollution incidents are always a high risk for such a system, and large amounts of water would be lost through evaporation.

Emergency measures Following two successive years of drought in southern England, in 1997 some urgent measures were implemented.

- Trials of huge plastic bags that float on the sea and can be used to store as much as 10 million litres of emergency water supplies. The emergency reservoirs are towed by tugs from areas where water is more plentiful.
- Proposals by Southern Water to install a desalinisation plant in Kent. This would remove salt from water in the chalk aquifer. The salt was originally sucked into the chalk as fresh water was pumped out by the National Coal Board during the 1970s, during their mining operations.
- The use of mobile desalinisation units to extract fresh water from the sea in southern England. A fixed desalinisation unit is to be located on the Norfolk coast.

Effective steps must be taken to reduce water-waste and to decrease our personal consumption. New sources of supply must be found or arrangements made to transfer water from areas of surplus to areas of deficit. If these actions are not implemented, millions of Britons will face frequent and formal restrictions on their use of water. Bans on car-washing and the use of garden sprinklers and hosepipes will become a part of everyday life. Supplies may even be cut off and water rationed from standpipes in the road.

Review

8 Of the four actions described above, which do you think is likely to be the most cost-effective? Give reasons for your answer.

Water supply issues in developing countries

Figure 5.7
India – collecting the daily water supply

So far, this chapter has dealt mainly with water supply issues in the UK. When we experience drought and consequent water shortages, we may suffer some temporary inconvenience from restrictions on water use. But in many less developed countries the unreliability of rainfall, and the consequent lack of water in some years, can result in widespread hardship and even famine. Overcoming the problems of inadequate public water supplies in developing countries has therefore been a major priority for development schemes paid for by the World Bank and more developed countries.

Such schemes often combine several uses for water – domestic supply, industrial use, irrigation and the production of hydro-electric power. Examples can be quoted from most parts of the developing world. Three very different case studies, all from India, are presented below. The largest, the Narmada River scheme, illustrates the arguments surrounding many large-scale projects, which are heavily criticised by some as an unsustainable and inappropriate use of water resources. This is contrasted with a successful small-scale project at Adgaon. Finally, the problems of urban water supply and sewage disposal are illustrated by Mumbai.

Case study: The Narmada River project

In a major attempt to solve the drought problems experienced by north-west India, the Indian government has embarked upon a huge but highly controversial project. Originally part-funded by the World Bank, the project began in the mid-1980s and was expected to take some 12 years to complete. The Narmada River project is located in Gujarat State **(5.8)**. It involves constructing 30 large dams, 135 medium-sized ones and over 3000 small ones. The main Sardar Sarovar dam, 1210 metres long and 139 metres high, will alone use 6 million m^3 of concrete.

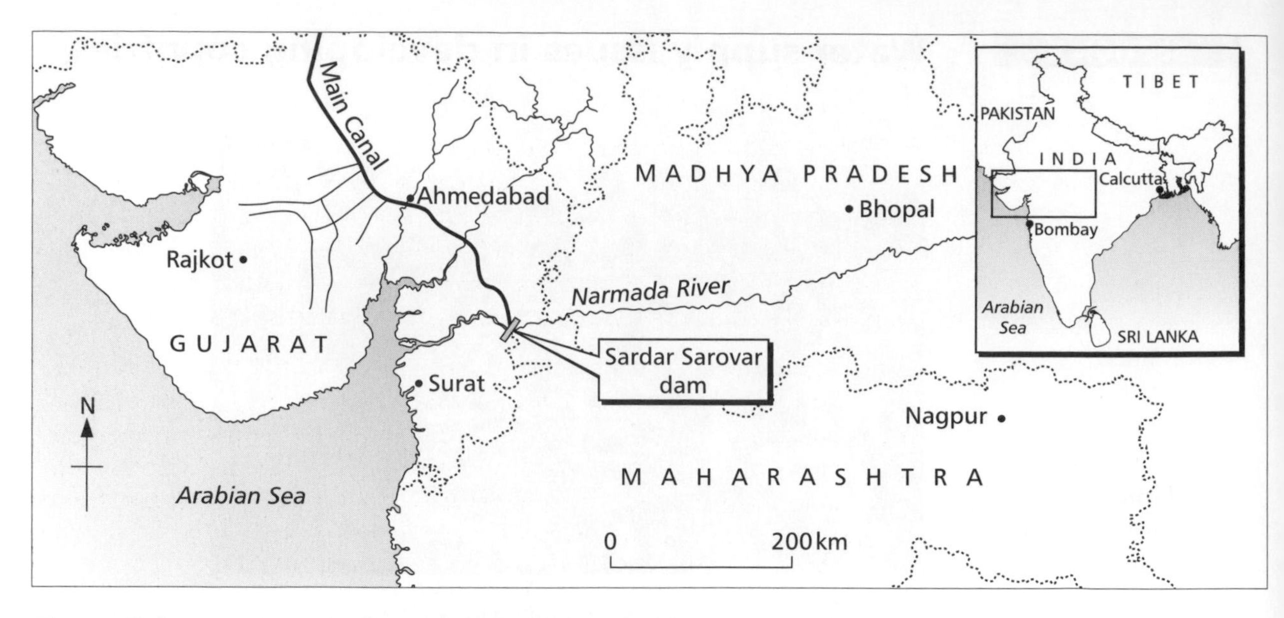

Figure 5.8
The location of the Narmada River project

The project has several objectives:

- to provide drinking water to 135 urban centres and 8214 villages
- to provide water to irrigate 1.9 million ha of land in the drought-stricken areas of Gujarat, especially Saurashta and Kutch
- to generate 1450MW of hydro-electric power.

The Sardar Sarovar dam and the many minor dams will retain excess monsoon flood waters and distribute them during the dry season via an extensive network of canals.

The project was originally granted US$450 million of funds by the World Bank, but was severely criticised during an official enquiry carried out in 1991–92. The report accused Indian officials of failing to satisfy many of the criteria laid down by the World Bank when the project was first agreed.

The enquiry made four major criticisms:

- the costs are far in excess of those originally projected
- the number of people displaced by the project has been grossly under-estimated
- inadequate arrangements have been made for the rehabilitation of the displaced people
- the environmental impacts have not been properly considered or adequately addressed.

As a result of these criticisms, the World Bank withdrew its support in 1993. Since then, the project has been forced to continue with funds provided solely by the Federal Government of India.

When the project began it was stated that only 6500 families would be ousted by the waters retained by the various dams. However, it is now known that at least 40 000 families will actually be displaced – a minimum of 160 000 people – and a further 140 000 are likely to be affected by the construction of the canals. Many of the people displaced by the scheme are 'tribal' folk with no title to the land they have been occupying for many generations. Because of this, they have not been classified as 'dam affected', and therefore are not eligible for resettlement.

In addition to the disruption of human lives, an estimated 100 000ha of forest will be submerged. This will destroy the habitat of many species of endangered plant, bird and mammal, including the Chinkara (a rare gazelle), and tigers, when much of the Sariska Tiger Reserve is drowned. Further areas of forest will have to be cleared in order to resettle the large numbers of people displaced by the scheme and to create irrigated farmland.

From the moment it was originally proposed in the 1970s, there has been strong local opposition led by the Save the Narmada Movement. Critics claim that, in addition to major disruption of the lives of the displaced people, too much water will be lost by evaporation and much of the potential irrigated land will actually receive no water. There is also likely to be severe salinisation, silting and waterlogging.

Recently, the project has come in for yet more criticism as the safety of the Sardar Sarovar dam has been questioned. During the 1994 and 1995 monsoon rains, the foot of the dam was badly damaged by excessive scouring. The latest episode in this scheme was the suspension of construction work in 1995 pending the outcome of a major court case to resolve a conflict between Gujarat and Madhya Pradesh states over the sharing of the Narmada's waters and the eventual height of the dam. At the time of writing (1997) the dispute has still not been settled.

Case study: A small-scale water supply scheme at Adgaon

The village of Adgaon in Maharashtra state lies some 270km south of the controversial Narmada River scheme. In 1985 this area was faced with similar drought problems to those of Gujarat, but a very different solution has been implemented. In normal years, about 500mm of rain falls during the monsoon from the end of June to mid-October, but in 1987 less than 300mm fell. Water levels in Adgaon's 153 wells fell dramatically, and many became totally dry. Tests showed that there was no further water to be had, even at depths of 90m beneath the surface. Streams had dried out and soil was being eroded.

A Swiss-funded non-governmental organisation worked with the villagers to overcome the problem. A series of small-scale measures were taken to conserve water:

- low earth banks were built along the contours
- erosion gullies were filled in
- small dams were constructed across stream beds.

The aim of all these initiatives was to trap water where it fell and to retain it in the soil for as long as possible. The villagers planted many trees including neem and banana and agreed to protect them from grazing livestock.

Today, the wells have permanent water once again. Streams flow throughout the year and fish are caught in once-dried-up streams. There are shady avenues of trees, and there has been no increase in malaria as the neem trees have insect-repellent properties, keeping mosquitoes at bay. Not a single person has been displaced by the scheme and, rather than drowning forests, new woodlands have been created. Resource management has become a local task and a responsibility which the whole community accepts.

Much has been achieved at Adgaon, at a total cost of only US$50 000 spread over three years – a tiny fraction of the Narmada project's budget. Both schemes aim to eliminate the problems of drought, but one is on a vast scale with much opposition and still to be completed. The other is small, already successful and receiving enthusiastic local support and cooperation. Large dams have a relatively short but troubled history and it has been suggested that major schemes like the Narmada River project are inappropriate and unsustainable, creating more environmental problems than they solve.

Figure 5.9 The strain on an inadequate water supply: washing clothes in an outflow pipe

Case study: Water supply and sewage disposal problems in Mumbai

With as many as 14 million people living in greater Mumbai (formerly Bombay), solving the challenges of sewage disposal and a clean water supply are the city authorities' major problems **(5.9)**. In the slum areas of the city, water supplies are grossly inadequate. A recent survey showed that there are over 200 users to every tap. In one area a single tap supplies more than 8000 people. Women living in these areas must get up at 3 or 4 a.m. to get a place in the queue for their 15 litres of water – all that is used by the average slum family in a day. The collection of this modest amount of water often takes several hours.

Over half of Mumbai's population lives in slums or on the pavements, and more than 2 million people have no access at all to a toilet facility. The city produces 2000 million litres of sewage each day. Much of the 1040km network of sewers is over 100 years old and huge amounts of money must be spent on maintenance and replacement. Untreated sewage often flows into open drains and water courses – a constant breeding-ground for diarrhoea, dysentery and infectious hepatitis. Leakages from sewers to water pipes that contaminate the water supply are not uncommon. Several of the main sewers discharge their untreated effluent directly into the sea, often less than a kilometre from the shore. This causes massive pollution and contamination of the coastline and its beaches. No sea bathing is possible here.

With the help of a US$230 million loan from the World Bank, the city authorities are making strenuous efforts to upgrade the system with the installation of new sewage pumping stations and treatment and disposal facilities. However, the scheme will not be completed until late in 2003. In the meantime, the hardship and squalor continue.

Review

9 Both developed and developing countries experience droughts. Are the causes the same in both cases?

10 'Small is beautiful.' How far is this the key to successful water management:
a in developing countries
b in developed countries?

11 Assume that you have been appointed as a consultant to advise the metropolitan authorities in Mumbai (formerly Bombay) on water supply and sewage issues. The city authorities need your advice to help them decide which their top priorities for expenditure should be:
a improvements to the water supply, or
b improvements to the sewage disposal system.

Prepare a presentation, using suitable graphic techniques, which illustrates your advice and the reasons for it.

Additional sources of information may be found in magazines such as *Business India* (available in most large libraries), *The New Internationalist* (see May 1997), and the Internet – see site at: http://theory.tifr.res.in/bombay/amenities/water/

There are other sites with information on this topic including that of the World Bank.

SECTION F

Water pollution

The essential need for abundant supplies of water has been stressed. However, it is not just quantity that is important – there is quality too. Both ground and surface water supplies are contaminated by human activities, with pollutants entering at several points in the hydrological cycle. Such pollution includes:

- dissolved nitrates and phosphates from artificial fertilisers, sewage and farm slurry disposal
- heavy metals, including lead, mercury and cadmium from manufacturing processes
- pesticide residues from agriculture and horticulture
- increased saline content as salts are drawn towards the surface in arid areas by evaporation of irrigation water
- acidification as sulphur dioxide and other waste gases in the atmosphere are dissolved, forming acid rain.

In some parts of Britain water supplies contain dissolved chemicals such as:

- industrial effluents
- leached fertilisers and other chemicals applied to the land
- farm effluents and animal waste
- raw sewage and effluent from sewage treatment plants
- chemicals derived from the gradual breakdown of waste in landfill sites.

Figure 5.10 Factors contributing to eutrophication

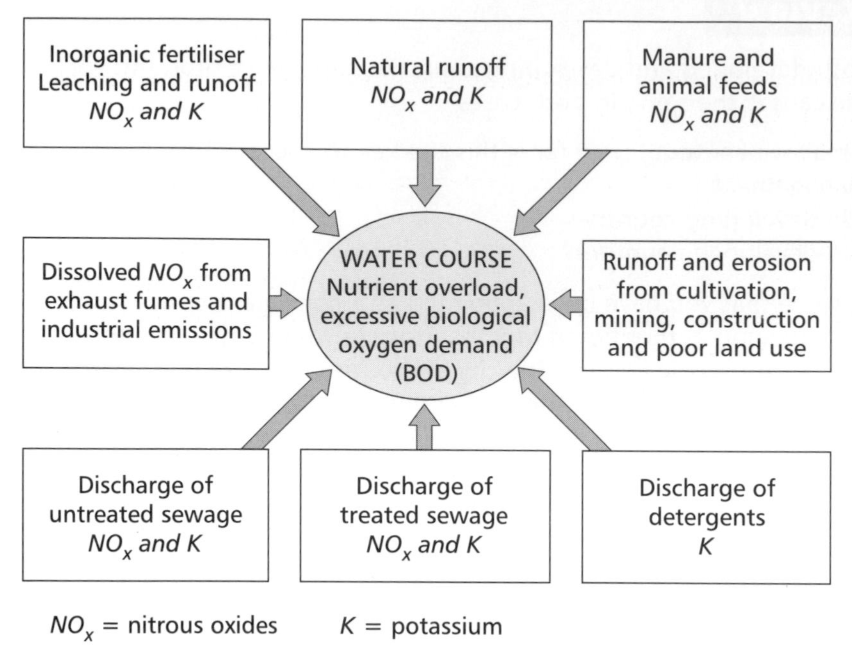

This sort of pollution causes a variety of problems including eutrophication **(5.10)**. When excessive supplies of plant nutrients (nitrates and phosphates) are present in water, plants that thrive in a low-nutrient environment die, but algae and other plants are stimulated into excessive growth. This upsets the ecological balance of surface water systems. Thus eutrophication leads to clogged water channels, reduced light penetration through the water and increased demand for oxygen dissolved in water (the BOD). This ultimately causes fish and other water organisms to suffocate.

To overcome this problem in domestic water supplies, Thames Water has had to install new filter systems. These clean the water that is abstracted from the River Thames and stored in London's reservoirs. This new system can cope efficiently with large quantities and does not become clogged by green algae, a problem that bedevilled the old system during hot weather. Much of the water consumed in the London area is recycled, having been used previously in such places as Oxford and Reading and returned to the Thames for further use down-river after thorough cleansing and processing. However, dissolved phosphates and nitrates are expensive to remove and the high levels present in London's water have led to eutrophication, causing algal blooms that have choked reservoirs and pipes.

Case study: The Dutch manure mountain

Intensification of farming methods is one of the main sources of nitrate and phosphate pollution of water supplies. The Netherlands has one of the highest levels of artificial fertiliser application in the world, with nitrates applied at around 218kg/ha and phosphates at 42kg/ha. It also has some 120 million farm animals on its relatively small land area. These produce over 110 million tonnes of manure each year – a veritable manure 'mountain', only a half of which can be effectively used for agricultural purposes. Manure disposal has become a major environmental problem and, coupled with artificial fertilisers, is a major cause of eutrophication. In many areas, groundwater can no longer be used for drinking water. Heath and dune vegetation has been destroyed by increasing nutrient levels in the water-table.

It has been found recently that there is a link between high levels of nitrate in drinking water and diabetes in children. This is a particular issue in rural areas where leached fertilisers can greatly increase nitrate levels in groundwater supplies. In the UK, farmers are being encouraged to reduce chemical inputs, by the establishment of nitrate-sensitive areas (NSAs). Research suggests that nitrate leaching can be effectively reduced by maintaining a crop cover on farmland during the winter. Strict regulations have been introduced to control the storage and disposal of silage effluent and animal slurries, with fines of up to £20 000 if water courses are polluted.

In conclusion, it would seem that water supply is a problem in many parts of the world, no matter what their current level of development. The problem is two-sided – there is a shortfall in both quantity and quality. Certainly, water as a resource needs to be treated with much more care and attention. There is an obligation on all of us to adopt a much more responsible attitude and to strive towards a much more sustainable use of the resource.

Enquiry

1 If you were the director of a privatised water company faced with high levels of pollution in the water you collect, what measures would you propose for overcoming the problem? (Remember that, as a company director, you have to serve the interests of your shareholders as well as your customers. You must also answer calls coming from conservation organisations for improvements to the quality of water in rivers and the need to preserve wetlands.)

2 'Does it really matter if wetland habitats and their associated wildlife are destroyed by schemes to provide people with water?' Using information from this book and from outside sources such as water companies, English Nature, the RSPB and Wildlife Conservation Trusts, examine the different viewpoints held on this issue. Give reasons and examples in support of these viewpoints.

3 It has been proposed that the existing water crisis, with a deficit in the south and east but an excess in the north-west, can be solved by the transfer of water from one area to another by a 'water grid', using the existing network of rivers and canals. Examine the advantages and difficulties likely to result if such a scheme were to be adopted.
You will need to seek information from such sources as the water companies, the Environment Agency, English Nature and conservation organisations. Look, too, at such publications as *Geographical Magazine* and *New Scientist* for appropriate articles. There may also be information available on the Internet.

CHAPTER 6

Non-renewable energy resources

SECTION A

Introducing energy

Of all the demands made by people on the Earth's natural resources, it is the production and use of energy that is causing the most concern. Worldwide, the demand for energy increased by 3 per cent in 1996 alone. We are all users of energy: for transport, cooking, lighting and heating, powering washing machines and TVs. Domestic uses in the UK account for just over a quarter of all the energy consumed (**6.1**). The production of that energy creates 15 per cent of the UK's emissions of carbon dioxide, each home in the UK contributing some 22 kg of CO_2 to the atmosphere every day. The remaining three-quarters of the UK's energy is used by industry, commerce, and transport by road, rail, water and air.

	%
Space heating	67
Water heating	18
Appliances	9
Cooking	6

Figure 6.1 The main consumers of domestic energy in the UK

Transport alone accounts for 30 per cent of energy use in the UK, virtually all of which comes from oil. Among the various means of passenger transport, large cars are by far the heaviest consumers of energy per passenger mile (**6.2**). The graph **6.3** shows the changes that have occurred in transport demand over a 40-year period. The huge increase in the use of cars and vans is the most striking feature. In 1995, half the UK car-owners drove their cars at least once a day.

	Energy used by passenger transport (mj per passenger mile)
Large car	4.6
Aircraft	4.0
Motorcycle	3.4
Small car	2.7
Moped	1.6
Bus	1.4
Train	1.2
Cycle	0.5

Figure 6.2 Energy used by passenger transport

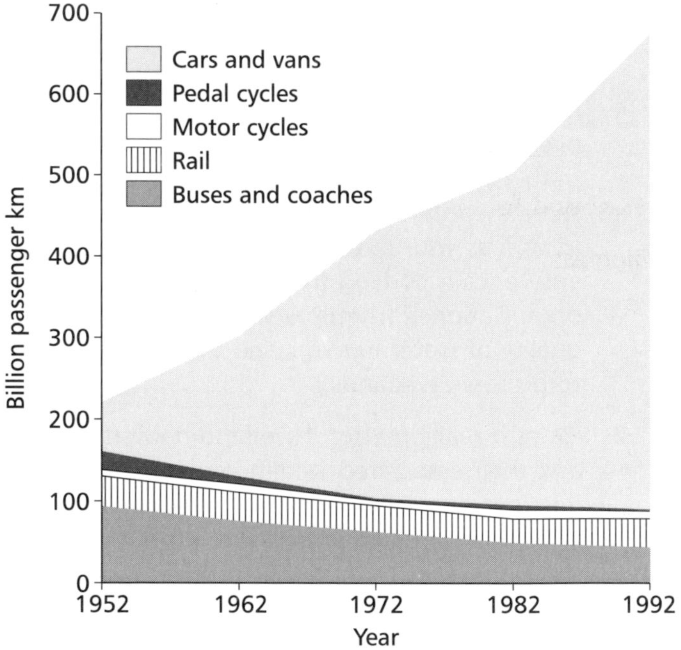

Figure 6.3 Growth in UK land transport demand, 1952–92

The demand for energy is very uneven across the world. This is part of the so-called **development gap**. Only about a quarter of the world's population live in the rich industrialised countries, but they use three-quarters of the world's energy. The USA contains only 6 per cent of the world's population, but it accounts for 30 per cent of the consumption of the Earth's energy resources. In fact, US per capita energy consumption is twice that in the UK and Japan. In contrast, India, which accounts for 20 per cent of the world's people, is responsible for using only 2 per cent of global energy. Here per capita energy consumption is one-fiftieth of that in the USA.

Only a part of the explanation of these differences in energy consumption can be put down to the fact that most of India enjoys a more tropical climate than the USA. Many buildings in the USA's warmer areas, such as California and Florida, are cooled by air-conditioning, and these states use almost as much per capita energy as the cooler states that need to heat their buildings more in winter. The major factor in the energy-consumption difference between India and the USA is the high rate of ownership and use of the car, and other energy-intensive transport systems, in the USA. When it comes to energy use, people in the rich industrialised countries impose a much greater ecological footprint on the environment than those living in the poorer developing nations. However, energy demand is now increasing in developing countries. This rise is the outcome of growing populations combined with development and industrialisation.

	World energy consumption (%)
Non-renewable	**80**
Oil	31
Coal	22
Natural gas	21
Nuclear energy*	6
Renewable	**20**
Biomass	13
HEP	6
Others	1

*Some people argue that nuclear energy consumes such small amounts of the resource uranium, it could also be classified as 'Renewable'.

Figure 6.4 Sources of world energy consumption, 1966

At the present time, the so-called **fossil fuels** – coal, oil and natural gas – are the most important sources of energy **(6.4)**. However, they are finite, **non-renewable** resources which, in the long term, will become exhausted. But energy can also be produced by harnessing the natural energy flows of the Earth. Because these flows are in a sense continuous, they may be regarded as **renewable** energy resources. The atmosphere may be exploited to yield wind power and solar energy. Moving water (rivers and tides) in the hydrosphere can be harnessed to generate electric power (HEP), while geothermal energy deep inside the Earth's crust (lithosphere) could also be used. Biomass within the biosphere is also capable of providing energy, for example in the form of fuelwood. Finally, there is nuclear energy. Technically, this should be classified as a non-renewable source of energy, since it is derived from a mineral resource, uranium. However, the amount of a mineral used to produce an enormous amount of nuclear energy is so small that there is little chance of the stocks ever becoming exhausted. This, coupled with the fact that nuclear fuel can to a certain extent be recycled, could provide some justification for regarding it as a renewable energy source.

In this chapter and in the next, we look systematically at a whole range of energy resources. What should emerge is that none of these resources is without disadvantages of some kind. It is a matter of measuring such costs against any benefits and using the balance between them to determine the acceptability or otherwise of each energy source. At the end of the day, however, the acid test is whether or not the particular energy can play its part in a sustainable energy strategy.

Review

1 Study the statistics in **6.1** and **6.5**. Write a short article for a local newspaper about the significance of these statistics. Include your recommendations for the personal actions that readers might take to reduce environmental problems. Make sure your article has an eye-catching headline.

2 Explain what is meant by a **sustainable energy strategy**.

SECTION B

Coal

Coal, oil and natural gas are the fossil remains of plants and animals that lived as part of the Earth's biosphere many millions of years ago. All organic matter is the result of photosynthesis, the food-making process that takes place in the leaf cells of green plants. This process locks up solar energy. Atoms of hydrogen and oxygen from water are combined with carbon dioxide (CO_2) from the atmosphere and various minerals from the soil to manufacture carbohydrates. When we burn fossil fuels, we are effectively reversing this process, which took place way back in the geological past. Heat energy is released, but so too are CO_2 and other greenhouse gases. It is estimated that it took nature roughly one million years to produce the amount of fossil fuel being burnt by the human population in just one year.

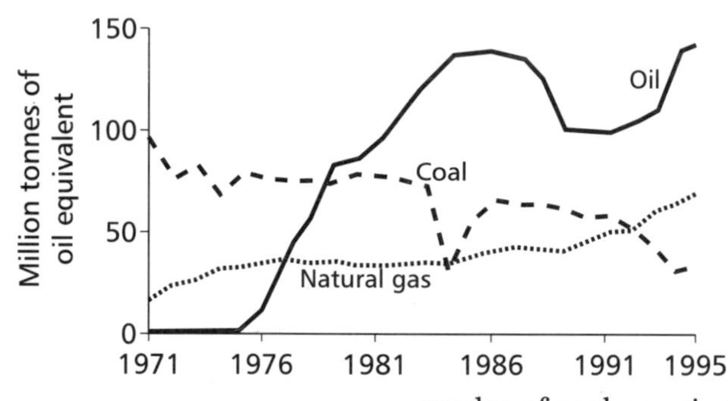

Figure 6.5 The changing production of primary fuels in the UK

It is clear that the relative importance of the different fossil fuels used to produce energy has changed over the centuries. Technology, population growth and development have been principally responsible for such shifts. In the UK, these shifts have been particularly marked in the last quarter of the 20th century **(6.5)**.

Coal is the largest of the fossil fuel resources and possibly the longest used. There are different grades of coal, ranging from poor-quality brown coal or lignite with many impurities (including sulphur), to anthracite which gives the highest energy output. Easy access to large amounts of coal formed the basis of the Industrial Revolution. This began in the UK in the second half of the 18th century following Abraham Darby's discovery of how to use coal in the smelting of iron. It was quickly followed by the construction of the first iron bridge, the invention of all manner of machines and the harnessing of steam to drive those machines, to propel transport and later to generate a secondary energy, electricity.

The use of coal reached its peak in the 1920s, but it has since been in decline, particularly since the Second World War. The most accessible coal deposits in Europe and North America have been worked out and, although there are huge known reserves, they are often too remote or too expensive to mine. Coal mining and the use of coal in power generation also incur huge environmental costs due to subsidence, landscape degradation, waste disposal, water and air pollution.

Although nearly a quarter of the world's energy is still provided by coal, it has been replaced to a large extent by oil, natural gas and nuclear energy in what has been called 'the rush from coal'. Despite the development of 'clean-coal technology', in which the most damaging emissions from the burning of coal have been reduced by up to 90 per cent, the number of pit closures continues to accelerate. A major factor is the declining demand for coal by electricity generating stations. The arguments set out in **6.6** appear to weigh increasingly against coal.

Figure 6.6 An evaluation of coal as a source of energy

Coal as an energy resource

The case **for**

- Coal is found in many places across the Earth.
- Although it is a finite resource, globally there are large proven reserves (at least 400 years' supply at current rates of use).
- It is an effective source of heat energy, easily exploited by burning in stoves or open fireplaces in the home, or pulverised for use in thermal power stations to produce electricity.
- Clean-coal technology has reduced emissions of noxious fumes and increased fuel efficiency.
- Coal produces a wide range of by-products, from dyes to artificial fibres.

The case **against**

- By burning coal, CO_2 is produced which, with other greenhouse gases, causes global warming.
- Other fumes are also released, including sulphur dioxide (SO_2) which produces acid rain.
- Fumes and particle emissions cause human health problems.
- Although widespread, coal is not evenly distributed globally.
- Coal mining produces huge quantities of waste.
- Opencast mining is unsightly and occupies large areas of land.
- Underground mining leads to subsidence, damaging buildings and transport networks.

Case study: The environmental impacts of coal mining in Poland

Coal accounts for nearly 90 per cent of the energy used in Poland and it is also a major export. Prior to recent political changes, both energy conservation policies and concern for the environment were largely neglected. Coal mining and the burning of coal in power stations were allowed to become major sources of pollution, with serious effects on the environment and the health of the local population. Indeed, Poland has been described as the most polluted country in the world.

Pollutants from the working of Polish coal are of three main types:

- atmospheric pollutants, especially dust from drilling and blasting activities, as most of the coal mines are opencast

- the release of methane gas (estimated at 5m^3 for every tonne of coal mined)
- liquid effluents, especially acidic water from the drainage of mines; this has seriously affected aquatic life, it is too acidic to be used for drinking water and too corrosive to be used in industrial processes.

In an attempt to reduce such pollution, the Polish government has recently set strict goals for the reduction of dust, methane and acid waters escaping from coal workings.

Review

3 a Suggest reasons for the switch from coal as the major resource for the production of energy.

b Identify the economic, social and environmental consequences of this switch.

SECTION C

Crude oil

Since the Second World War, crude oil has become the supreme source of the world's energy. It is used to heat our homes and offices, to fuel our cars and aeroplanes and to generate electricity. It accounts for 31 per cent of the world's consumption of energy.

Because of its geological location, extraction of crude oil requires massive investment in drilling and pumping equipment, pipelines, storage and port facilities, tankers and finally refineries where usable products are distilled from it. Globally, crude oil is even more unevenly distributed than coal. All too frequently it is found in areas remote from the main centres of population, and it has to be transported great distances by pipeline or tanker. Some of the environments in which oil is found are very difficult to work in. For example, the Alaskan oilfield is set in Arctic tundra where **permafrost** prevails. Oil rigs and pipelines must be specially constructed to overcome the unstable conditions of the **active layer** where surface thawing may occur in summer. If pipelines are not fully insulated they too thaw the active layer by absorbing solar radiation and because they carry warm crude oil. The North Sea is another hostile environment requiring the use of drilling platforms that are able to withstand strong winds and rough seas.

Most of the developed countries use more oil than they can produce from within their own territorial boundaries; much has to be imported. For this reason, crude oil has become a strategic and political 'hot potato', often resulting in military conflict and international financial crises. For example, the oil crises of 1973 and 1979/80 were created by the Organisation of Petroleum Exporting Countries (OPEC) when for political reasons they suddenly raised the price of their crude oil. In 1991 the Gulf War again concentrated the minds of the Western world on the vulnerability of their dependence on oil supplies from the Middle East. Along with increasing environmental concerns, this has become another factor in hastening the search for alternative energy from renewable rather than finite resources, and the drive towards improved energy efficiency.

Figure 6.7 An evaluation of crude oil as a source of energy

Crude oil as an energy resource

The case **for**

- Oil is easily transported overland by pipeline.
- It is an effective and flexible source of energy, used by the internal combustion engine, in power stations to produce electricity, and for heating buildings.
- It is a valuable raw material for a wide range of products, from fertilisers to plastics.

The case **against**

- Oil is a finite resource, more unevenly distributed than coal and therefore is strategically and politically vulnerable.
- It is often located in hostile physical environments requiring major investment and advanced technology for successful exploitation.
- Igniting oil produces CO_2 (which contributes to global warming), carbon monoxide and unburned hydro-carbons which pollute the atmosphere, produce smog and cause asthma and other human health problems.
- Tanker accidents and oil spills at sea endanger wildlife and damage beaches.

Review

4 What were the consequences of the oil crises in 1973 and 1979/80?

5 Which countries are the major producers of crude oil, and which are the major consumers?

SECTION D

Natural gas

Natural gas originates in the same way as oil, and is often found in the same rock formations. It consists of the more volatile hydro-carbons, including methane, and was probably formed under higher temperatures than oil.

Currently there is a world surplus in supplies of natural gas and, therefore, it is relatively cheap. It pollutes the atmosphere less than oil, although 'sour' gas contains sulphur which must be removed. Of all energy resources, natural gas has seen the fastest growth on a global scale in recent years. It can be used for the same purposes as oil and coal and already 20 per cent of Europe's energy production is gas-based. In the UK there a has been a very rapid conversion of power stations from burning coal or oil to the new combined-cycle gas turbines, in the so-called 'dash for gas'.

Figure 6.8 An evaluation of natural gas as a source of energy

Natural gas as an energy resource

The case **for**

- Gas is cheaper than crude oil.
- It is less damaging to the atmosphere than burning oil or coal – it produces less CO_2 for the same amount of energy produced.
- It is an efficient source of energy.

The case **against**

- Known reserves are limited, estimated at about 120 years at current rates of use.
- Gas is vulnerable to leakage – perhaps up to 5 per cent of the total tapped escapes.
- It gives off methane, a greenhouse gas.
- It suffers the same production problems as oil as it occurs in similar locations and rock strata.

Case study: The growth of natural gas exploitation – a 'macaroni of pipelines'!

1 The Yamal pipeline

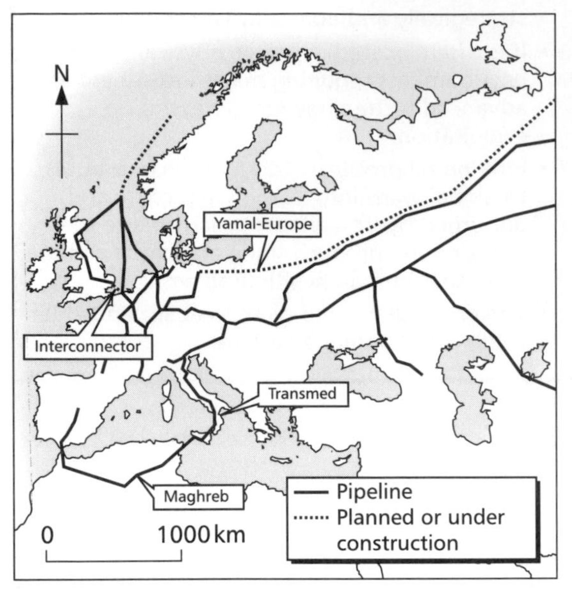

Figure 6.9
Europe's gas pipelines

It is estimated that 80 per cent of the world's known reserves of natural gas occur in the huge natural gas deposits of Russia. As it is found in places remote from the main concentrations of population, pipelines are being laid to transport it the huge distances to its main markets. The most recent of these is the Yamal pipeline stretching 5900km from Siberia to Germany. With a capacity of 67 billion m^3 per year, it has been constructed to tap the huge natural gas reserves located beneath the Yamal peninsula.

It is managed by Gazprom, a company that in 1995 supplied 23 per cent of all the gas consumed in Europe. The Yamal peninsula reserves are estimated at 30 000 billion m^3. That is enough to supply the whole of Western Europe for 115 years at current rates of consumption. Already 20 per cent of Europe's energy production is gas-based.

2 The Maghreb pipeline

The Groningen gasfield in north-east Netherlands is scheduled for exhaustion during the next decade. To offset this, BP is investing US$3 billion to produce gas from Algeria in North Africa. The Transmed pipeline already pipes gas from North Africa to Europe but a new pipeline – the Maghreb – will take it 2500km to Gibraltar, Spain and Portugal at a construction cost of $3.5 billion. By the year 2000 the pipeline links will be extended to France and Germany, by which time the pipeline as a whole will be supplying up to 10 per cent of Europe's needs.

3 The Interconnector

Another pipeline carries North Sea natural gas from the UK to France, Belgium and the Netherlands.

Review

6 What are the advantages and disadvantages of oil and natural gas as sources of energy? Why is natural gas now favoured over oil and coal as a fuel source for electricity generation?

SECTION E

Nuclear power

Nuclear power is produced by the fission of atoms using radioactive uranium. This releases large amounts of energy, causing chain reactions in other uranium atoms. The heat produced by these reactions is used to create steam to drive the turbines that generate electric power. Very small amounts of uranium are required – 100g produces as much energy as one tonne of oil.

Twenty years ago the prospects for nuclear power worldwide were looking good, even though doubts about its safety had been expressed by conservation organisations such as Friends of the Earth and Greenpeace. In the mid-1990s, 431 nuclear reactors in 44 countries generated 6 per cent of the world's energy consumption **(6.4)**. However, accidents at Three Mile Island (USA) in 1979 and at Chernobyl in the Ukraine in 1986 proved the critics right. Public opinion has since been a powerful force in slowing down the nuclear programme. In Germany it has been halted altogether, whilst in the USA plans for their 110th nuclear power station have been shelved.

Another major problem for the nuclear power industry is the fact that it produces radioactive waste. This needs to be stored where it cannot harm the environment during its radioactive life, which lasts for centuries. Waste ranges from very low-level contamination (workers' protective clothing, for example) through medium-level waste that may need to be encased in concrete, to high-level radioactive materials. The last includes spent uranium rods and plutonium which must be reprocessed, or stored in purpose-built long-term sites; both options are very expensive. Decommissioning costs at the end of the productive life of a nuclear power station are also very high.

Case study: The nuclear reactor explosion at Chernobyl

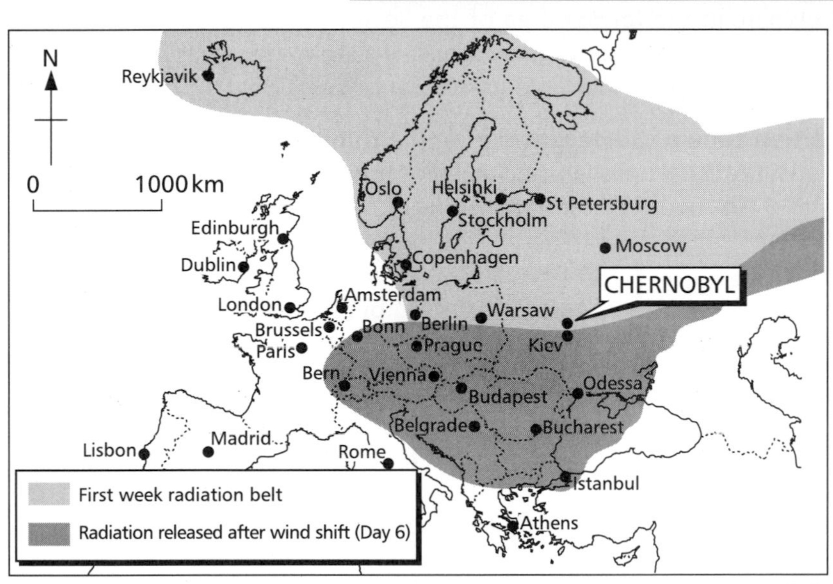

Figure 6.10 The spread of fallout from the Chernobyl accident

26 April 1986 – a black day for the nuclear power industry. The number 4 reactor in the nuclear power plant at Chernobyl, just 88km from Kiev in the Ukraine, developed a major fault. Nuclear fuel in the reactor overheated, causing an explosion and releasing a plume of radioactive elements into the atmosphere. It remains the world's worst nuclear power disaster.

The particular elements making up the radioactive plume were plutonium and the radioactive isotopes strontium-90, iodine-131 and caesium-137. Winds carried the plume thousands of kilometres to the north and west, bringing fallout to a wide area of northern Europe and the former Soviet Union, in heavy, polluted rainfall **(6.10)**.

In Wales and the English Lake District, some 2300km away, there was heavy rainfall on 2/3 May, causing deposition of radioactive fallout on vegetation. Several hundred sheep had to be destroyed because they had grazed on contaminated grass. They were declared 'unfit for human consumption' with levels of radioactivity recorded at up to four times the intervention limit. The British government had to pay out £2.1 million to farmers under various compensation schemes. Scandinavia received much higher levels of radioactive fallout from Chernobyl than the UK. In Lapland reindeer ingested large amounts of radioactive fallout by grazing on the pollution-sensitive lichens that form their diet. In most years, in the autumn, the Lapp reindeer herders slaughter some 35 per cent of their animals for meat, but several months after the Chernobyl disaster, most of the animals were found to contain more than 30 times the level of radioactivity considered safe for human consumption. Fish in the area were also declared unfit to eat. As a safety measure, the Scandinavian governments recommended that the herders should slaughter and dispose of 80 per cent of their animals. As the contaminated lichens would continue to pose a radioactive hazard for a minimum of ten years, the herders were faced with a hard choice – either eat contaminated meat or accept the end of their normal way of life.

In the Ukraine, many people involved in fighting the fire and in the clean-up operation have since died of acute radiation syndrome. Some estimates put the number as high as 7000. Many others experienced radiation burns or are suffering from thyroid cancer and other malignant tumours. Many Ukrainian children have since been born with defects.

Two other nuclear reactors at Chernobyl are still operating. The workers, swathed in protective clothing, are brought in daily by a shuttle bus. These reactors are of the same flawed design as the one that exploded, and elsewhere in the former area of the Soviet Union 13 other reactors of the same type continue to produce electricity under safety conditions that would not be regarded adequate in the West.

An exclusion zone of 30km was declared around Chernobyl. This area is supposed to remain uninhabited. In fact about 650 people – drop-out settlers and evacuees who simply returned home – are prepared to accept the risk of living in the area. A concrete hood has been built over the failed reactor to prevent further radioactive escape. However, this structure is unstable, with cracks and holes resulting from shoddy workmanship. It is leaking radioactivity. There are now plans to bring in a West European company which will use a foam spray of silicon elastomers that can resist radiation for 200 years, to seal the cracks and prevent dust leakage. A second concrete hood will be built to enclose the first.

Figure 6.11 An evaluation of nuclear power as a source of energy

Nuclear power as an energy resource

The case **for**

- It does not cause air pollution.
- It does not contribute to the greenhouse effect.
- Huge investments are already made in research and development.
- Only small amounts of uranium are used.
- Running costs are low.

The case **against**

- Costs of technological research and development are high.
- Power stations are very costly to build, and even more costly to decommission.
- There is a risk of radioactive waste contaminating the environment ('active' for up to 100 years).
- There is a risk of nuclear accidents.
- Radioactive fallout causes deaths, cancers and other abnormalities in living things, often far from the source.
- There are huge problems of disposal of radioactive waste.

Review

7 Discuss the view that nuclear energy provides an environmentally acceptable alternative to the use of fossil fuels.

8 Debate the following motion:
'This house believes that, as a potential source of energy, nuclear power is an option only for the industrialised countries.'

Figure 6.12 Using non-renewable energy resources causes air pollution and high CO_2 emissions

To sum up, it is clear that the world today continues to derive the greater part of its energy from non-renewable resources. There are two major worries here. First, there are the environmental costs of burning fossil fuels and the risks associated with nuclear power. Secondly, there is the inescapable fact that these resources are finite. At present, exploration and advances in technology readily convert stocks into reserves, but the day will come when stocks run out. The best that can be done now is to ensure a careful and efficient use of those remaining stocks and to develop alternative sources of energy.

Enquiry

1 What are the likely economic, social and environmental costs of not adopting a sustainable approach to energy use?

2 'Think globally, but act locally.' Draw up a list of measures that your school or community should take that would contribute to a reduction in local demand for energy.

3 Examine the factors that influence the utilisation of different energy resources.

CHAPTER 7

Renewable sources of energy

In this chapter, the spotlight falls on those sources of power that harness the natural energies of the global system. They are quite varied in character and are as yet relatively unexploited. Despite their renewable and sustainable character, their present contribution to the global energy budget is insignificant. Why is this?

SECTION A

Hydro-electric power (HEP)

Hydro-electric schemes harness the force of running water to generate electricity. They usually involve the construction of large dams on major river systems in order to create reservoirs. Below the reservoir, power-generating turbines are installed, rotated by the gravitational force of water that is released from the reservoir. Such schemes may be combined with other objectives such as irrigation programmes and water supply.

Just over 6 per cent of the world's energy consumption is based on hydro-electric power.

At first sight, HEP may seem to be a clean, environmentally friendly source of energy, and one that is infinitely renewable. However, there are often major environmental and social disadvantages. The construction of the dam requires huge capital investment and the reservoir created may drown valuable land – it might be forest, farmland or wildlife habitats, or contain sites of historic, archaeological or cultural significance. In most cases, people are displaced. Indeed, in some cases large towns may be drowned, as in the Three Gorges project in China. Most schemes have a limited lifespan because silt is trapped behind the dam and gradually fills the reservoir. There is also a risk of dam failure due to construction faults or earthquakes.

Figure 7.1 An evaluation of large-scale HEP schemes

Large-scale HEP schemes

The case **for**

- Water is a renewable resource.
- It is a clean and non-polluting source of energy.
- Large schemes may also provide water for irrigation and for domestic and industrial supply.
- Reservoirs may be used for recreation.

The case **against**

- Construction requires major capital expenditure.
- Construction work may damage the environment.
- Natural ecosystems and wildlife may be disrupted or destroyed.
- People must be resettled if settlements are drowned and inhabitants are displaced.
- Agricultural land may be submerged.
- Archaeological, historic and cultural heritage may be destroyed.
- Human life may be endangered if the dam breaks.
- Some schemes have been blamed for increases in earthquakes.

Case study: The Three Gorges dam, China

When construction is completed in the year 2003, the Three Gorges dam in China will be the world's largest HEP scheme, eight times more productive than Egypt's Aswan dam. This major development is taking place at Sandouping on the Daning River, a main tributary of China's mighty Yangtze River. The dam is being constructed between the steep valley sides of Xiling Gorge, the downstream end of the Three Gorges. When completed, a reservoir 632km long and up to 120m deep will have been created.

The project has several purposes:

- to generate 18 000 MW of HEP
- to provide water for irrigation
- to prevent flooding of the densely-populated coastal plain downstream from the gorge
- to improve navigation
- to create opportunities for fish production.

Figure 7.2 A model of the Three Gorges dam

It is hoped that the HEP produced by the Three Gorges dam will be a major factor in reducing China's emissions of greenhouse gases and the incidence of acid rain. These are currently produced by inefficient, coal-burning thermal power stations. However, the project is also creating problems. For example, when the dam is finished, more than 1.2 million people from 300 towns and villages will be displaced as the waters of the reservoir rise. Wushan, with a population of 90 000, will be completely destroyed, as will much of Wanxian (140 000) and Fuling (80 000). The peasant farmers who at present cultivate fields of fertile black earth alongside the Daning River will be forced to live in huge blocks of flats that are being built high above the level of the reservoir. It is planned that farming should continue, but this will only be possible by terracing the barren hillsides above the dam – a task that will be done almost entirely by hand. While Wushan is of little historic or cultural importance, archaeologists are concerned that elsewhere significant historic remains will be lost. Archaeologists complain that there has been too little time and too little cash to fully investigate the area and to excavate key locations.

Some critics of the scheme claim that it is unnecessary. The air pollution created by the existing thermal power stations could be greatly reduced by improved efficiency both in the power stations themselves and in the use of power in factories and homes. Other critics claim that the colossal weight of water in the dam could create crustal instability, triggering earthquakes. Another fear is that the huge quantities of silt currently carried by the Daning River will be deposited in the reservoir, thus reducing its productive life to only a few decades. This silting-up will also deprive areas downstream of valuable alluvial deposits, and cause increased erosion. Terraced farming of the steep hillsides will further increase the amount of silt entering the reservoir.

Botanists, too, are concerned about the environmental impact of the scheme. Presently they are scouring the area, seeking to save some 400 rare plant species that might otherwise be lost. Zoologists are anxious for the future of the highly endangered Chinese sturgeon, the finless porpoise, the remaining 300 white flag dolphins and the 500 Chinese alligators that inhabit the river. The shallow Poyang lake, which will be drowned by the rising waters of the reservoir, is the winter home of the spectacular Siberian crane. With fewer than 2000 individuals left, this is one of the world's most endangered bird species. There appears to be no other suitable habitat available in China to which these displaced birds migrate.

It is important to make a distinction between large-scale HEP schemes such as the Three Gorges project, and much smaller projects that might be installed by a single family or small village, which simply make use of the energy from fast-flowing water. These do not suffer from the same disadvantages as the large schemes; they are far less disruptive to a river system as a whole and do not displace people or drown historic and cultural sites. However, they can only be installed in hilly areas where there is sufficient, non-seasonal rainfall to provide the necessary constant flow.

Figure 7.3 An evaluation of small-scale HEP schemes

Small-scale HEP schemes

The case **for**

- They are cheap to install and maintain.
- The technology is simple and safe.
- They are non-polluting.
- Small schemes are suitable for remote hilly areas, provided there is sufficient rainfall.

The case **against**

- They require a constant supply of fast-flowing water.
- They must be small-scale if environmental damage is to be avoided.

Review

1 How do you explain the fact that only a small fraction of the world's running water has been harnessed to generate HEP?

2 Assess the relative merits of large-scale and small-scale HEP schemes. You should refer to specific examples of large-scale schemes.

Biomass

This is the production of energy from the biosphere using organic material such as plant material, dung or other animal matter. The direct burning of wood or other organic material is the most obvious and longest-serving form of biofuel. Many people, especially in developing countries, are still dependent on wood as their main fuel for cooking. Even in a huge city like Mumbai (Bombay), nearly half the population still cook on wood fires. The other use of organic material is to place it in some form of 'digester' to produce biogas (mainly methane) or to make wood alcohol.

Biogas digesters may be small-scale, providing sufficient gas to meet the needs of a family or small group of dwellings. But there are much larger schemes, often landfill sites, that produce gas, again mainly methane, from decomposition of the organic waste present in household waste. Nearly 90 per cent of the UK's garbage is disposed of in landfill sites or by building rubbish mounds, but at most sites the methane is simply allowed to escape into the atmosphere. Methane is one of the more potent 'greenhouse gases', trapping 26 times more long-wave radiation than carbon dioxide. It therefore makes good sense to use it by capping the filled site with clay, piping the gas and using it as fuel. When methane is burnt, carbon dioxide is released but in rather smaller quantities than from fossil fuels. Biogas may also be produced by processing raw sewage.

Case study: Landfill gas at Stewartby and Brogborough, near Bedford

Near Bedford two industries – the London Brick Company and Shanks McEwan, respectively making bricks and disposing of waste – have combined to make beneficial use of landfill gas. This is a biogas produced from decaying organic rubbish in landfill sites.

The quarrying of clay for the manufacture of bricks results in huge open pits. These are often flooded and in their after-use may be used for recreation and other leisure activities. However, at Stewartby and Brogborough, near Bedford, the disused clay pits are now being used for the disposal of household refuse collected from Bedford and the surrounding suburbs and villages. When a pit is filled, the rubbish it contains is capped with gas-proof clay. As it decays, landfill gas is produced. This is collected by vertical polythene pipes sunk into the waste, and transported by a surface network of pipes to a filtration point, where the gas is cleaned, cooled and compressed.

Landfill gas produced by decaying organic rubbish consists of 60 per cent methane and 39 per cent carbon dioxide, with traces of oxygen and nitrogen. It has a calorific value of 550 BTUs per cubic foot, very similar to that of natural gas.

As a result, the London Brick Company has made huge savings on its fuel bills by using this landfill gas to heat its brick kilns. In fact, so much gas is now being produced here that a 14MW power station has been installed at Brogborough which uses landfill gas to generate electricity.

Case study: Low-cost biogas plant in Moyar, an Indian village

Moyar is a small village within the Mudumalai Wildlife Sanctuary of the Western Ghats, a mountainous area in the south-west of India. Traditionally, most of the energy requirements of the area – mainly for cooking – have come from burning fuelwood gathered from the local forest. Few homes can afford to pay for electricity and only about one in five homes are connected to the state grid. However, there are major concerns about the adverse impact on the forest of fuelwood collection.

Figure 7.4 A low-cost biogas plant in Moyar

In order to reduce pressure on the forest, the local authorities have provided grants to assist the construction of small, low-cost biogas plants in many of the villages. These simple digesters are built from local materials and consist of a cylinder and a gas-proof cover **(7.4)**. This is filled with a variety of organic material, much of it agricultural waste such as straw, dead leaves, dung and excrement. The biogas produced is about 60 per cent methane.

The introduction of biogas to Moyar has considerably reduced the workload of the women in the village, who used to spend several hours each day gathering fuelwood. Another advantage of the digester is that once the digestion process has finished, a rich, odourless compost remains which is a valuable manure.

Figure 7.5 An evaluation of biomass as a source of energy

Energy from biomass

The case **for**

- It is constantly renewable.
- Usually it is cheap.
- Waste organic material is recycled.
- Matter remaining after processing in small biogas units can be a valuable fertiliser.
- Small biogas plants are very suitable for rural areas.
- There is little pollution – less CO_2 is produced than from fossil fuels.

The case **against**

- There is some pollution, with CO_2 released – but this would be released anyway in natural decay processes.
- Use of wood as a fuel can cause deforestation.
- Crops grown as fuel may take the place of other crops.
- It is essentially a small-scale resource.

Review

3 'There is greater scope for developing energy from biomass and decaying organic material in the developing world.' How far do you agree with this statement?

SECTION C

Solar power

Areas receiving long hours of sunshine have an obvious potential source of renewable energy if it can be harnessed. In cloudier countries such as the UK the potential of solar energy may be rather less. At present there are three main methods by which the sun's energy is used as a power source:

- by focusing the sun's rays onto photovoltaic cells to produce electricity
- by focusing the sun's rays onto water and producing steam to drive turbines that generate electricity
- by retaining and storing solar heat in heat-absorbing materials.

Some of the current harnessing of solar energy is very small-scale, as in solar-powered calculators or watches, for example, and many satellites have solar panels to power the instruments they carry. It is also possible to locate solar panels on the roofs of homes. This can be an effective means of heating water 'free' (apart from the installation costs) as a supplement to the mains supply provided by oil, gas or electricity.

In contrast, there are some large-scale projects such as the Kramer Junction solar power plant in the Mojave Desert, USA. Here, on a site covering 406ha, large parabolic reflectors concentrate the sun's rays to produce steam. This in turn drives the turbines capable of generating 250MW of electric power. There is a huge potential for more solar-power plants of this kind in the sunnier parts of the world. It is even possible that, in the not-too-distant future, solar-powered vehicles can be developed.

Figure 7.6 An evaluation of solar power as a source of energy

Solar power

The case **for**

- It is pollution free.
- The sun is a continuous and never-ending natural resource, although less reliable in higher latitudes and places with cloudy climates and seasons.
- It is a safe source of energy.
- Once the solar energy power generation or storage system has been installed it can operate indefinitely, more or less free of cost, making it suitable for poor areas.
- If more power is required, the system can be constantly expanded.
- Some systems are lightweight and easily carried by nomadic peoples.

The case **against**

- In cloudy areas it can only be used as a supplement to other sources of energy.
- Initial installation costs are relatively high.
- Energy is only produced in daylight hours, so batteries and/or thermal storage are needed for night use.
- More research and development is needed for the technology to develop its full potential.

SECTION D

Tidal power

In some places with a large tidal range, the rise and fall of the tide is being exploited to rotate electric generators set in a barrage built across an estuary. For example, there is a successful tidal power plant established across the estuary of the River Rance near St Malo in Brittany. Electricity is generated as water flows both in and out of the estuary, although there is a short pause in production at high and low tides before the turbines turn again, but in the reverse direction.

Tidal power

The case **for**	The case **against**
• It is a never-ending resource, clean, safe and reliable. • The power produced is cheap, after huge initial costs. • Upstream areas are protected from tidal surges. • The reservoir behind the barrage could be used for recreation or fish farming.	• Initial construction costs are very high. • There is a pause in power production at high and low tides. • The estuary ecosystems both above and below the barrage are altered, possibly destroyed – a disaster for estuary-dependent wading birds and wildfowl. • Breeding grounds of many fish and crustacean species are lost.

Figure 7.7 An evaluation of tidal power

It has been estimated that if such a barrage were to be constructed across the Severn Estuary between England and Wales, it would be possible to generate about 6 per cent of the UK's electric power requirements. Although tidal power is a continuously renewable and highly reliable energy source from the hydrosphere, the construction of such a barrage would create many other environmental problems, especially to significant wildlife populations.

Review

4 A proposal has been made to build a huge tidal barrage across a major river estuary in the UK. What interest groups would you expect to **(a)** support the proposal, and **(b)** oppose it? Why do they hold these views?

SECTION E

Wind power

Historically, windmills were used to grind corn or to pump water. The modern wind-powered generator has a much greater efficiency and has the potential to become the cheapest 'clean energy' option by exploiting natural air movement in the atmosphere. It is an endlessly renewable power source which, unlike fossil fuels, produces no harmful chemical emissions. It is an energy source that is being rapidly developed in many parts of the world **(7.8)**.

Figure 7.8
A wind farm in upland Wales

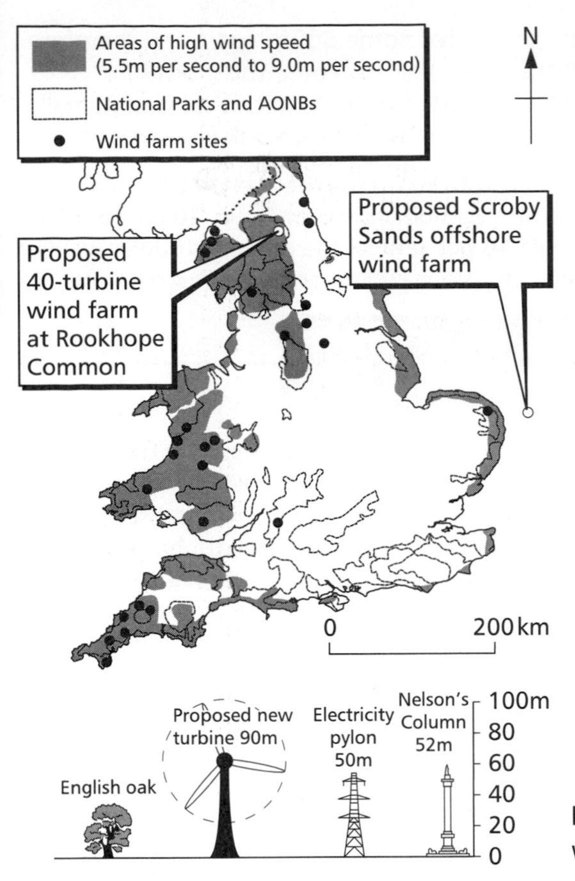

Figure 7.9 The distribution of wind farms in England and Wales

In the UK today, wind-powered generators supply the electricity needs of about 300 000 people **(7.9)**. If the equivalent amount of power had been generated by burning fossil fuels, some 400 000 tonnes of carbon dioxide would have been released into the atmosphere. However, the modern windmill is visually intrusive and is only efficient if it is located in a windy area with average wind speeds of more than 5m per second. Ideally they should be located on a plateau above gentle slopes to avoid excessive turbulence. They are also noisy. Even at a distance of 500m, a generator creates 40 decibels of noise under normal wind conditions. Despite their 'clean' image, very strong objections have been raised to the construction of wind farms in Areas of Outstanding Natural Beauty (AONB). It is unfortunate that such areas offer some of the best sites for wind-farm developments.

Case study: Proposed wind farm at Rookhope Common, Co. Durham

A proposal by National Wind Power to build Britain's largest wind farm at Rookhope Common **(7.9)** is being opposed by several major conservation organisations on the grounds that such an unsightly development would be totally inappropriate in this AONB. The Council for the Protection of Rural England, the Ramblers' Association and the Council for National Parks are leading the protest. If approved, construction will begin in late 1998. Jonathan Porritt, former Director of Friends of the Earth and a very keen supporter of alternative energy, is reported in *The Times* as saying that this scheme would be seriously 'damaging to the overall case for this crucial source of renewable energy'.

The development would consist of 40 turbines, each more than 90m high (one and a half times the height of Nelson's Column) and each capable of generating 1.5MW, bringing the total capacity of the development to 60MW. The largest machines currently operating in the UK in 1997 are only 600kW (1000kW = 1MW). The proposed development would be built on moorland above Weardale in the beautiful, heather-clad northern Pennines. It is a very exposed location with winds averaging 10m per second. National Wind Power claim it is an ideal site.

The individual generators must be located some 300m apart and therefore would be spread across a considerable area. However, the individual 'footprint' (the amount of land occupied by each tower) is relatively small, so 98 per cent of the area could also be used for livestock grazing.

It has been calculated that even if all future wind-power generators were the same massive size as those proposed for Rookhope Common, 10 000 of them would be required to generate just 10 per cent of the country's power needs. This would reduce carbon dioxide emissions by little more than 3 per cent.

Case study: Plan for an offshore wind farm in Norfolk

Wind power

The case **for**
- It is a plentiful, renewable, clean and cheap source of energy.
- It is suitable for all windy areas of the world.
- It does not depend on long hours of sunshine, and operates night and day.
- The technology is simple and safe.
- It is ideal for areas that lack other sources of energy and which would otherwise need to import fossil fuels.

The case **against**
- Generators are unsightly and obtrusive in areas of outstanding natural beauty.
- Noise disturbance is created in otherwise quiet places.
- Further research is needed to improve the efficiency of the technology.
- It is only suitable for areas of constant wind not subject to turbulence.
- Each windmill has a limited generating capacity.

Figure 7.10 An evaluation of wind power as a source of energy

In 1996 a plan by PowerGen to install 25 huge wind turbines, each 60m high, on Scroby Sands, a sandbank located some 2km offshore from Great Yarmouth, has run into considerable opposition **(7.10)**. Although sufficiently far from land to overcome problems of noise, and the offshore location would not spoil the landscape, wildlife conservationists from the Sea Mammal Research Unit and the RSPB are concerned that its presence would disturb the basking area on the sands of some 200 grey and Atlantic seals and the feeding grounds of seabirds, including the now rare little tern. Both the seals and the terns enjoy special protection under European law.

However, other conservation groups such as the Council for the Preservation of Rural England and Friends of the Earth consider that the scheme may be beneficial. The turbines would be located at the northern end of Scroby Sands in a shallow area that is always submerged and well away from the seals' basking area. In their view, the development would create job opportunities and a chance for Britain to take a lead in the development of offshore wind-farm technology. The argument continues.

Review

5 Study 7.9.

a Explain the distribution of wind farms in the UK shown by the map.

b Why do you think there are so few wind farms located in coastal areas, even though they are windy?

SECTION F

Geothermal energy

In some parts of the world – Iceland, Japan and Mexico, for example – heat from the Earth's interior can be detected close to the surface. This geothermal energy is a potentially limitless source of heat provided by the lithosphere, either directly in the rocks or in the form of very hot water or steam or created by contact with these rocks. These can provide energy for the space-heating of homes, offices and other buildings, or can be piped to the surface to drive turbines that generate electricity. However, the harnessing of geothermal energy does pose problems.

Geothermal energy

The case **for**

- It is clean, but there is possible minor pollution from the release of noxious gases, such as hydrogen sulphide, from beneath the surface.
- It is a safe and constant source.
- It is cost-efficient in suitable locations once it has been tapped.

The case **against**

- It is very localised and usually of limited capacity.
- The initial drilling to tap the heat source is very noisy.
- Large amounts of water are needed when drilling.
- Disposal of drilling fluids needs a large body of water.
- There is a risk of pollution from toxic gases and saline water.

Figure 7.11 An evaluation of geothermal energy as a source of energy

Review

6 Find out which countries make use of thermal energy, and plot them on a world map. Comment on the distribution shown by your map and suggest some reasons for it.

SECTION G

Conclusion

Perhaps the most surprising conclusion to emerge from this study of renewable energy resources is that they remain so relatively undeveloped. They still provide only 20 per cent of the world's energy consumption, and much of this is from fuelwood. This might seem to fly in the face of good sense. What could be wiser than tapping nature's continuous energy flows? One factor that appears to tip the scales is the economics of exploiting these renewable sources of energy. They do not seem to be able to offer the same economies of scale as coal, oil or gas. Also, whilst the use of renewable energy resources is more environmentally friendly than that of non-renewable resources, it is not without environmental costs.

Is the energy situation likely to change in the 21st century? The short answer is – not dramatically! However, at a time when there is an increasing awareness of the need for a sustainable use of resources, we can expect the non-renewable sources to satisfy an increasing proportion of the world's energy needs. That rise is unlikely to eclipse the contribution made by non-renewable sources, but the hope is that the latter will be used with ever-increasing efficiency and care.

Enquiry

1 a Using the information and case studies in this chapter and **Chapter 6**, propose a set of criteria which might be used to evaluate alternative sources of energy from both renewable and non-renewable resources.

b Produce a table or spreadsheet that matches the alternative sources against your criteria, and explain your results.

c Explain why non-renewable energy resources have been able to achieve economies of scale but these cannot be matched by renewable energy resources.

d Using the information you have collected in **(a)**, **(b)** and **(c)**, and quoting examples, discuss the statement: 'There is no such thing as a perfect source of energy'.

2 The 'Greening Committee' of your school has suggested it should reduce the school's environmental impact, and make savings on its fuel bills, by installing solar power panels on the roof. The Chairman of the Governors, who owns a firm selling heating oil, is on record as saying, 'Solar power is a neat idea, but there are too many practical difficulties.' Is he right? What other options might be considered to save fuel bills and reduce environmental impact?

3 As a geographer you have been asked to investigate whether there is a site in your local area suitable for the development of a wind farm. After a careful study of the OS map, and using your local knowledge of the environment and local people's attitudes, write a report of your findings and the supporting evidence.

Mineral resources

SECTION A

Introduction

Modern society is highly dependent on a wide variety of minerals. These are natural resources found in the lithosphere or rocks of the Earth's crust. They range from the fossil fuels and uranium needed for energy production to construction materials such as clay, sand, gravel and building stone. They also include industrial minerals such as soda ash and lime, iron and copper, gold and platinum. Minerals are essentially finite, non-renewable resources, but some – such as building materials and most metals – can be recycled or re-used.

With over 100 different minerals required regularly by modern industry, no nation is completely self-sufficient, however richly endowed it may be with some. Mineral wealth is very unevenly distributed across the world, and depends on geological factors. The human resources of technology and skills, and the economic or capital resources necessary for working the minerals, are also unevenly distributed.

Minerals pass through a number of different stages during their life-cycle (**8.1**):

- exploration to locate the resource
- evaluation of whether or not it is worthwhile exploiting
- extraction of the mineral
- processing for use or manufacture into goods
- disposal of waste
- disposal of manufactured goods after their useful life.

At each stage in the life-cycle there is some kind of environmental impact (**8.2**).

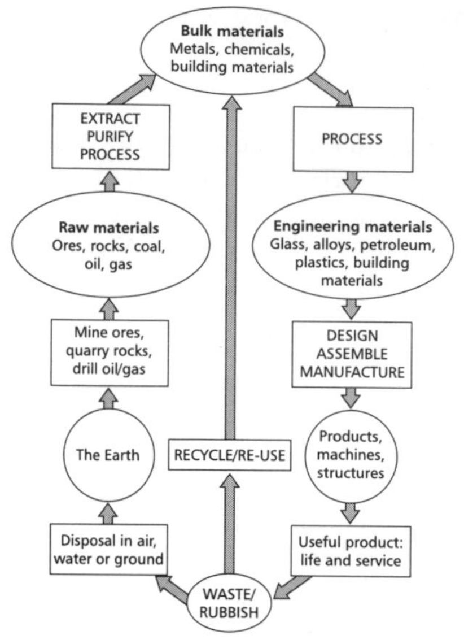

Figure 8.1 The life-cycle of minerals

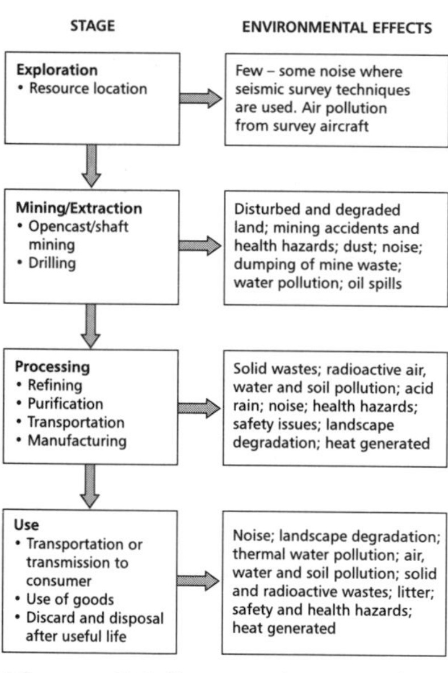

Figure 8.2 Some environmental impacts of mineral exploitation

Review

1 Find out what minerals other than oil and natural gas are imported into the UK. Is the UK self-sufficient in any minerals?

2 Apart from coal, oil, gas and metals, what other minerals do you find in your home?

3 Some car manufacturers have stressed that their vehicles are made of materials that can be recycled at the end of the car's useful life. What are the advantages and disadvantages of this recycling?

Mineral exploration and extraction

Mineral exploration requires a knowledge of geology and analytical or discovery surveys to detect rocks and appropriate structures in which mineral-bearing deposits are likely to be found. Remote-sensing techniques including aerial and satellite photography are often used. Some mineral deposits are discovered by other means. For example, metallic ores may cause anomalies in the Earth's magnetic or gravitational fields and these may be detected by instruments attached to aircraft or satellites. Likely locations are sometimes more closely investigated by means of seismic surveys and the analysis of core samples taken from boreholes.

	% of total surface workings area
Sand and gravel	31
Ironstone	15
Limestone	12
Opencast coal	9
Clay and shale	9
Other minerals	24

Figure 8.3 Surface mineral workings in England – total area 16 000ha

Minerals in liquid (crude oil) or gaseous form (natural gas) can be pumped and piped to the surface, but solid material must be quarried or mined. The nature of that material and the depth at which it occurs below the surface will determine whether mining or quarrying techniques are used. Those close to the surface can be obtained from quarries or surface pits **(8.3).** Opencast working is obviously a much less expensive process than adit tunnels which follow seams into a hillside, or deep mines that use vertical shafts to reach resources buried beneath the surface. Surface pits are particularly common for 'abundant' minerals such as sand and gravel (used as aggregates in concrete and in building roads and buildings), limestone (used as building stone and in a variety of industrial processes), chalk (often the basis for cement manufacture) and clay (for pottery and brick-making). However, in some locations coal and metallic ores are also obtained from open pits. No matter what extraction technique is used, the working of minerals can – and most often does – create environmental destruction and dereliction over a wide area.

Where land is a scarce resource, there will be pressures for the sites of exhausted mineral workings to be put to some new use. Opencast pits and quarries can be filled and restored as farmland. About 50 per cent of the area used for mineral extraction in the UK is restored for this purpose. Holes in the ground are also at a premium for waste disposal. The use of former clay pits near Bedford for this purpose, and subsequent biogas production, are described in the case study on pages 73–74. Often pits are so deep that they reach down to the local water-table and fill with water. During quarrying operations this water has to be pumped out, but disused, flooded pits can become valuable recreational areas for sailing, water-skiing and angling. They also provide important habitats for waterbirds and other wildlife.

Case study: Gravel pits at Little Paxton, Cambridgeshire

Gravels are found on the floodplain of the River Ouse. These have been quarried for several decades as a source of road-building material and as aggregate for use in concrete. Prior to quarrying the surface soil is bulldozed and piled up as banks at the edge of the area that is to be worked. The sand and gravel is excavated by draglines and floating dredgers, and transported by conveyor belt to be washed, sifted and graded by stone size before being stored or loaded by huge funnel-shaped hoppers into lorries for transport to the consumer.

Figure 8.4 Gravel pits at Little Paxton:
(a) shortly after gravel extraction ceased
(b) several years afterwards

Because of their low-lying location close to the River Ouse, the pits penetrate the local water-table and are flooded. In many parts of the country, after such pits have been worked out they are filled with waste (perhaps domestic rubbish) and the topsoil replaced. The site may then be cultivated or used as building land, although this has caused problems due to seepage of methane gas (landfill gas) from the decaying rubbish beneath. However, at Little Paxton the flooded pits have become an important local nature reserve, providing a habitat for such birds as the common tern, kingfisher, heron and many kinds of wildfowl **(8.4)**. The site is also well known for its nightingales, which nest in spring in the bankside vegetation. Other pits in the area are used for sailing and angling.

Few minerals can be obtained without first removing the overburden of soil and rock. The extraction of minerals also produces waste, and this must be disposed of. Solid waste can be in the form of dust, but most is dumped as unsightly spoil-tips which cause habitat loss, risk of pollution and, if not properly constructed, slope failure. One estimate suggests that the amount of unwanted soil and rock resulting from mineral extraction which has to be disposed of globally each year amounts to a staggering 3000 billion tonnes.

Some waste may be liquid and therefore a potential pollutant of drainage systems and the sea. Rainwater percolating through exposed rocks and spoil-tips can also be a threat, particularly in the case of sulphur-rich coal-tips. Coal spoil readily reacts chemically with water to produce sulphuric acid which may subsequently enter nearby streams and rivers. The acid can also percolate into groundwater in aquifers, causing contamination of drinking water. Some waste may be gaseous and cause atmospheric pollution.

Case study: Quarrying proposals for the Isle of Harris

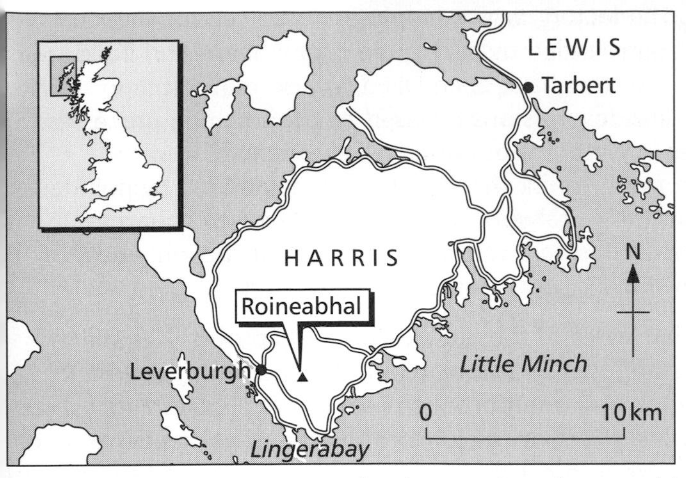

Figure 8.5 Superquarry on Harris in the Outer Hebrides

In 1993, Redland Aggregates put forward a proposal to open a huge quarry at Lingerabay on the Isle of Harris. It would extract road-building stone. The cost of this development in the Outer Hebrides was put at £70 million. An estimated 600 million tonnes of rock would be extracted over 60 years, eventually removing a mountain and creating a new loch some 2km^2 in extent. The Western Isles Council was initially in favour of the project, stressing that many jobs would be created for local people. However, large numbers of islanders opposed the idea, one claiming that the quarry would produce 'a huge pall of death-grey dust that would find its way into every corner of our homes and into our lungs, shortening our lives'. Others stressed the noise and damage that would be caused to the environment, to fishing and tourism.

Review

4 Examine the case for and against in-filling flooded sand and gravel workings after they are worked out.

5 What is meant by a 'NIMBY'? Would you have supported or opposed the proposed stone quarry on the Isle of Harris **(8.5)**? Give reasons for your answer.

SECTION C

Mineral processing

Few minerals are found in a form pure enough for immediate use. They usually require some kind of refining or processing **(8.2)**. Depending on the mineral, the refining process can be a major cause of atmospheric, water and soil pollution. Smelting of copper and nickel, for example, can release large quantities of sulphur dioxide unless large investments are made in pollution control equipment.

Case study: The mining and refining of copper and nickel in Siberia

With a population of a quarter of a million, Norilsk is Russia's largest mining town. It was established in the 1930s by the former Soviet Union, its sole function being the mining and production of metals. Norilsk lies deep in the coniferous forest of Siberia – though perhaps it would be truer to say in 'former coniferous forest', for little of the original cover is still alive. A forest of dead trees stretches for many kilometres around the town.

Figure 8.6 Part of a forest devastated by pollution from the Norilsk metalworks

The rocks of the area are rich in copper-nickel ore and coal which, most unusually, occur within a few hundred metres of each other. These resources are quarried and the ore is refined in the Norilsk metalworks. The factory, which employs 90 per cent of the local workforce, is surrounded by bare quarry spoil-heaps and bulldozed overburden. The trees have been killed by acid rain resulting from the sulphur dioxide emissions released by the smelting processes. This dissolves in water vapour and falls as sulphuric acid. Downstream from Norilsk the local river is stained red by pollutants draining from the metalworks and pumped from the quarries. In winter, temperatures here can fall to –50 °C, but the whiteness of freshly fallen snow is soon masked by a black crust.

It is hoped that some of the nickel company's profits (it is still 48 per cent state-owned) will be ploughed back into the area to reduce pollution and to enforce some of Russia's increasingly strict though far from effective environmental laws. Local residents fear the problems are so great that little less than a full-scale social revolution could reduce them.

Review

6 The processing of most mineral resources causes environmental pollution. Find out about the processes involved and potential pollution caused by:
a processing chalk and limestone to make cement
b smelting copper and nickel ores
c converting bauxite into aluminium
d manufacturing steel from iron ore.
Which of these causes the greatest environmental damage?

7 List some examples of where plastics have replaced metals in manufactured goods. Is the production and disposal of plastics at the end of the item's life cycle more or less damaging to the environment?

SECTION D

Waste disposal

The exploitation of natural resources inevitably produces waste, some of it toxic, some of it radioactive. Waste is an issue at two stages in the life-cycle of a mineral **(8.1)**. First, there is the creation of waste at the extraction, refining and processing stage – that is, before the minerals are used in the production of manufactured goods, which can range from tea cups to aircraft, from metal cans to jewellery. Secondly, there comes a time when the manufactured goods reach the end of their useful life. In the more developed countries we live in a high-waste/throw-away society. Packaging is a major source of waste, but consumer goods like fridges, cars and TV sets have a limited life and also become waste. In England and Wales, 827kg of waste per household was collected in 1995/96, an increase of 37kg per household over 1994/95. Some 80 per cent of this waste is still buried in landfill sites, with all the attendant risks of ground and water pollution, whilst much of the remainder is incinerated, thereby adding to atmospheric pollution. In order to reduce environmental damage and prolong supplies of natural resources, environmentalists are advocating the '3 Rs' – Reduce waste, Re-use and Recycle.

Enormous quantities of minerals and other raw materials are wasted if they are disposed of in dumps. Recycling has therefore become fashionable, particularly in dealing with household waste. Paper, plastic, glass and aluminium drinks cans are being collected by many local authorities in the UK for recycling. Collecting scrap metal has been going on far longer. Today, however, because of the costs of working and processing minerals and because of growing concern about their non-renewable nature, people are making a good living from salvage. Defunct motor vehicles and household equipment, old factory plant and redundant buildings are all being scavenged for their metal.

Although there is some reprocessing of nuclear fuels to reduce levels of radioactivity, disposal of radioactive waste poses serious problems – this issue was examined in **Chapter 6**. The key question remains: Who can be sure that the arrangements made for the storage of waste will remain secure for the hundreds of years it will take for it to lose its radioactivity?

In summary, then, we have become aware of the environmental costs associated with the exploitation of mineral resources. That, and the fact that the resources are essentially non-renewable, should provide the spur for modern society to move in two directions. First, to research and develop alternative and more environmentally friendly materials; and second, to recycle as much as possible those mineral resources that have already been extracted.

Enquiry

1. Explain why the disposal of waste by both landfill and incineration have their environmental costs. Is it possible to safely dispose of all waste by these two means?
2. Make a list of the pros and cons associated with the recycling of metals.
3. **a** Make a list of six major environmental consequences of exploiting mineral resources.
   b For each of these, suggest measures that might be taken to reduce the harmful environmental impact.
4. Discuss the assertion that: 'Recycling is not the solution to reducing our consumption of finite resources. It merely delays their inevitable exhaustion, and in the process causes further environmental damage.' If recycling is not the answer, what is?

CHAPTER 9

Conclusion

SECTION A

Think globally, act locally

How we choose to live on our fragile planet Earth, and the choices we make in exploiting its natural resources, really do matter. In most cases, our use of any natural resource results in an adverse impact on the environment and on the Earth's life-support systems. Sustainable development is the only way we have of ensuring a safe future for human life and the biodiversity on which we rely. But there are major problems.

The natural resources we need are not evenly distributed. This creates local and international disparities, of extreme poverty in some areas and huge affluence in others. The gap between the rich and the poor nations is growing, but the less developed nations are beginning to demand a fairer share of the Earth's limited natural resources. Our global life-support systems are threatened, on the one hand by overpopulation in poorer countries, and on the other by over-consumption in the richer nations.

The interlocking problems of population growth, resource depletion, environmental degradation and pollution are serious, but they are not necessarily unresolvable. The achievement of a sustainable future may require international solutions – that is, by 'thinking globally'. However, some of the case studies have shown that small-scale projects to overcome local environmental difficulties can be very successful and have a major role to play. By 'acting locally', individuals can benefit directly from the actions they take; they are personally involved. A sense of responsibility and ownership is created. This in turn strengthens the chances of a successful resolution of the difficulties.

Very often we blame others for the Earth's environmental problems and fail to recognise our own part in causing them. Global warming, for example, is being caused by human behaviour and, if we are to turn the situation around, we will all be required to make profound changes to our behaviour and life-styles. Car-owners know that their vehicles are a major source of the carbon dioxide and other emissions causing the atmospheric pollution that is leading to global warming. A look at car windscreen stickers reveals that many motorists support organisations that campaign against the greenhouse effect, so why does the conversation stop when it is suggested that their behaviour should change and that cars must be used less often? Could public transport be used as an alternative? Could the journey be made on foot or bicycle? Is the journey really necessary in the first place? As individuals we may feel there is little we can do, or that our own small action will make no difference. But if we all take actions to save resources – by reducing consumption, recycling and easing the pressure we are putting on the environment – much can be achieved.

Figure 9.1 Acting locally

Individual actions will be even more effective if they are backed by policy initiatives at local, national and international levels. Despite considerable research, much uncertainty remains about the long-term impacts on the environment of such factors as the loss of biodiversity, biotechnology, water and air pollution. Whilst this uncertainty prevails, most conservationists agree that everything possible should be done to maintain, or even enhance, present population levels and geographical distributions of species. This is known as the 'precautionary principle'. It means, for example, restricting (perhaps even completely banning) activities that use dangerous materials or spread potentially dangerous pollutants. So long as the scientific understanding of their effects is incomplete, it is better to be safe than sorry.

SECTION B

The Earth Summit on Environment and Development, and Agenda 21

In an attempt to find solutions to the Earth's environmental and resource exploitation problems, the leaders of 153 nations met at an Earth Summit Conference on Environment and Development held in Rio de Janeiro in 1992. The major points of agreement were set out as a comprehensive and far-reaching programme for sustainable development. This is known as **Agenda 21** – a blueprint for the 21st century.

Its key premise is that sustainable development is crucial. The improvement or maintenance of our living standards should not be allowed to destroy the natural resources on which those standards are based. One of the key tests of sustainability is, as we have seen in **Chapter 2**, the maintenance of biodiversity. The Earth Summit agreed that economic development is not sustainable development unless it also conserves biodiversity. All government policies for the economic sectors of agriculture, forestry, fisheries, energy and transport must therefore include biodiversity objectives.

Environmental problems do not recognise national boundaries. Rainforest destruction, global warming, depletion of the ozone layer, loss of biodiversity, drought and desertification have an implication for the whole world. No single country can solve these problems on its own. For this reason, it is essential that there is international cooperation. The Earth Summit agreed that national policies would be for sustainable use of the Earth's natural resources. In the UK the Government has published a *Strategy for Sustainable Development* and *Biodiversity – an Action Plan*, but much of their content has still to be implemented. Follow-up international conferences to Agenda 21 – New York (1997) and Kyoto (1998) – have also shown that progress is slow.

Perhaps the most appropriate conclusion for this study of the use and abuse of natural resources is to state the rights and principles of sustainability set out in Agenda 21:

- All human beings are entitled to a healthy and productive life in harmony with nature.
- All nations have a responsibility to reduce demand for natural resources.
- Unsustainable patterns of production and consumption should be eliminated.
- Non-renewable resources should be conserved by using them for essential purposes only.
- More use should be made of renewable resources.
- Pollution levels must be reduced.
- Damage to natural systems such as the hydrological cycle should be minimised, and natural ecosystems such as tropical rainforests conserved and maintained.
- It is the duty of the state to hold environmental resources in trust to benefit the public.
- The 'precautionary principle' should always be applied.
- Sustainability implies the principle of 'inter-generational equity' – that is, the needs of the present generation should be met without compromising the ability of future generations to meet their own needs.
- The principle of 'subsidiarity' should be applied – that is, making decisions locally rather than centrally.
- The 'polluter pays principle' should be enforced.

Enquiry

1 Give examples of why international actions are urgently needed to conserve natural resources.

2 Find out what initiatives have been taken by your local council to conserve natural resources. Have they been successful?

3 a Look at the list of principles from Agenda 21 set out above. Select the four principles that you believe to be the most important, and list them in rank order. Justify your choice.

b Look at a copy of the UK's *Strategy for Sustainable Development* and *Biodiversity – an Action Plan*, both published by the Department of the Environment. These are the UK government's response to the 1992 Rio Earth Summit. Make a list of the main actions called for in these plans. Find out from recent reports by the Department of the Environment (larger libraries have these in their reference section) how many suggested measures have actually been implemented.

c Draw up and implement your own Environmental Action Plan based on the enquiries you have made during your work with this book.

d Does your school have an environmental policy? If not, discuss with your teacher the possibilities and mechanisms for devising one. A useful reference is the Council for Environmental Education's publication, *Our World – Our Responsibility*.